SWIMMING
FOR
SENIORS

Edward J. Shea, PhD
Southern Illinois University—Carbondale

Leisure Press
Champaign, Illinois

Library of Congress Cataloging-in-Publication Data

Shea, Edward J.
    Swimming for seniors

    Bibliography: p.
    Includes index.
    1. Swimming for the aged.   I. Title.
GV837.3.S53   1986   797.2'1'0240565   85-23787
ISBN 0-88011-271-9

Developmental Editor: Sue Wilmoth, PhD
Production Director: Ernie Noa
Copy Editor: Rina Ullman
Typesetter: Brad Colson
Text Design: Julie Szamocki

Text Layout: Lezli Harris
Cover Design: Jack Davis
Cover Photo courtesy of Jim Corley
Printed By: United Graphics, Inc.

ISBN: 0-88011-271-9
Copyright © 1986 Edward J. Shea

Printed in the United States of America

10 9 8 7 6 5 4

Leisure Press
A Division of Human Kinetics Publishers, Inc.
Box 5076, Champaign, IL 61825-5076
1-800-747-4457

CONTENTS

ACKNOWLEDGMENTS

I would like to thank Thomas K. Cureton, Jr. and Charles E. Silvia for their extraordinary contributions in swimming and physical education. Their work has always been an inspiration to me as a teacher and coach, and much of the knowledge I used in writing this book is a reflection of my earlier years as their student.

I extend my gratitude to many senior swimmers whom I have had the privilege of teaching. My experiences with them and their encouragement were primary motivators for writing this text. These seniors taught me the important lessons of how to adapt swimming to the needs of seniors by individualizing programs and creating adaptations to conventional methods of performing swimming skills. These lessons are reflected in the instructional chapters of the text.

I am grateful for the kind and generous work Harold Friermood did on my manuscript. Dr. Friermood reviewed my manuscript in its early stages, offering helpful suggestions and adding his endorsement to my effort. Dr. Friermood has made excellent contributions to national and international physical fitness programs, and his support has been most encouraging and significant.

Thanks go to Sue Wilmoth, my developmental editor at Human Kinetics Publishers. She guided me through the entire project with patience, understanding, and helpfulness. I wish to thank Jacqueline Mueller for her artwork and for her high degree of personal application to the task.

I offer a gesture of thankfulness to publishers of all forms of scientific research. The accessibility of studies being performed by research scientists makes everyone's job of staying well-informed a plausible task.

FOREWORD

By Harold T. Friermood*

Swimming has long been recognized as an excellent activity to achieve physical fitness. Many books have been written on the proper skills and techniques needed to enhance one's swimming performance. No other book, however, interprets the fitness needs of mature adults and offers effective, individualized programs to meet their needs as well as *Swimming for Seniors*. The encouraging tone of the book is attributable to the author's years of being a top-level Masters swimmer as well as a professor of physical education. After years of direct involvement in competing with and teaching seniors to swim, Ed Shea shares his positive approach to swimming with others. Although the title is *Swimming for Seniors*, swimmers of all ages can benefit from the material the author presents.

---

*Harold T. Friermood served as the first executive Director of the Council for National Cooperation in Aquatics. This position followed his retirement from the headquarters staff of the National Board of the YMCA of the USA after 25 years as Senior Director for sport and health. Dr. Friermood has been the recipient of numerous national and international awards and citations for his distinguished service and leadership in aquatics, health, and educational organizations.

PREFACE

Authoritative reports indicate that exercising may delay the physiological processes normally associated with aging. There are also personal testimonies from senior swimmers to indicate that they are experiencing an improved quality of life. At 71 years of age, I have had a number of years of association with senior men and women who have turned to swimming for exercise and for enjoyment. Although they almost unanimously express wishes to pursue their own interests and desires, seniors are also concerned with improving their swimming skills. They often reach out for help, which reinforces their motivation to continue swimming and to even extend themselves for increased benefits. This text is designed to help seniors improve their swimming skills. *Swimming for Seniors* is a carefully designed, individualized swim-for-fitness program geared to enhance the quality of a senior's life.

The *Swimming for Seniors* program begins with the placement of seniors in swimming skill and fitness levels. The classification is self-determined on the basis of the starting ability of the senior without respect to age. Progress through the classification system is individually and easily measured and interpreted. There is no need for a distinction between men and women because of the common basis upon which classification and progress are determined. Comparison with other seniors may be made in an easy, convenient way.

Prescriptive swimming sessions are included for each classification. Seniors are taught to monitor the intensity of the workout, to set their own pace, and to plan their own program. Many of the basic principles used in designing the swim program were derived from biomedical, behavioral, and social scientific research, which suggests that some of the decremental aspects of aging may be modified with regular exercise.

One distinguishing feature of this swim program involves teaching seniors how to modify conventional strokes. A variety of swim strokes are presented, and the senior is encouraged to experiment with the strokes, seeking enjoyment and personal progress.

The senior swim program is designed for those who can swim. Although a swimmer may be too out of shape to swim the initial 20 to 25 yards, he or she can still enter the program. Just as the program is not designed for the master level competitive swimmer, neither is it restricted to the 55-year-and-older group of seniors. The program, although designed especially for seniors, may be of interest and assistance to others.

Instructors will find the content of the text to be an excellent guide for teaching and for the organization of programs adaptable to individuals. Exercises that can be done in or out of the water are presented in the last two chapters of the book. These exercises focus primarily on improving swimmers' flexibility and muscular strength. The strength and flexibility gained from these exercises will enhance swimming ability and will also carry over into daily activities.

Edward J. Shea

ABOUT THE AUTHOR

Ed Shea has an enviable record of achievement as a Masters swimmer. At 71, he is presently the U.S. Masters National Swimming Champion and a member of the All-American U.S. Masters Swim Team. He is the 1986 National YMCA Masters champion and record holder in all backstroke events.

Ed holds the national and American records for all backstroke events, both short and long course, and he holds the world's record in the 200-meter and 50-meter backstroke in his age division. The 1984 Top Ten rankings of U.S. Masters swimmers places him as number one in all backstroke events, while he ranks at the top position in world best performances.

Ed Shea's accomplishments are not limited to swimming. Dr. Shea also holds a remarkable record as a physical educator. He has served as chairman of the department of Physical Education for Men and the Department of Physical Education at Southern Illinois University, Carbondale, for 27 years. Dr. Shea has contributed extensive professional service in leadership positions. These positions include President of the American Academy of Physical Education and President of

the Illinois Assocation for Health, Physical Education, and Recreation. He is a member of the Governor's Advisory Council of Illinois on Health and Fitness and is a member of the Board of Directors of the National Amateur Athletic Union. He has received honor awards for the highest attainment of meritorious service from the American Alliance for Health, Physical Education, Recreation and Dance, the Illinois Association for Health, Physical Education and Recreation, and the National Amateur Athletic Union.

1 ENHANCING THE QUALITY OF LIFE

We all share a common experience in life—aging. We progress through the stages of development from birth to about 26 to 30 years of age, then experience a gradual leveling off and decline, and finally, death. This period of time, whether short or long, is marked by continuing change. The amount of scientific information explaining the aging process has been increasing in recent years. Through research and study, more attention is being given to the aging process; there appears to be increasing support for possibilities for enrichment of life and improving the quality of life through prescribed individual adaptations to each person's environment.

A consensus of expert judgment suggests that the paths of decline in physiological functions shown in Figure 1.1 can be positively influenced. It becomes largely a matter of individual

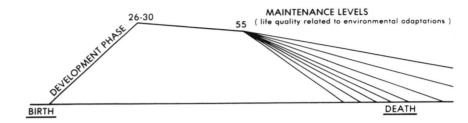

Figure 1.1 The direction in which physiological development is marked by a consistent increase from birth to 26-30 years of age followed by a slight levelling off and/or decline to be later indicated by optional directions of maintenance based upon individual choice of life regimens (life-styles). Age 55 arbitrarily chosen for meaningfulness in this presentation.

decision as to the degree of decline to be permitted.

There is support for the contention that the extension of the lifespan in the future will require more emphasis on health maintenance. There is also an abundance of evidence that healthful living and preventive medicine can retard the effects of aging and probably increase longevity. In recent years a good deal of attention has been directed

to the efforts of diet, exercise, and activity on retarding aging and on enriching the quality of life. A major finding of the last two decades regarding the retardation of aging stresses importance of remaining active, exercising to whatever degree is tolerable, and keeping busy. When people are no longer active, the prognosis for a long and healthy life is poor (Fries & Crapo, 1981). Such advice was dramatically expressed by an older aunt to her middle-aged niece when she wrote, "Amy, never grow old. Whenever you think you cannot do something, get up and do it."

Reasons seniors give for why they engage in swimming programs reveal that concern for their health is very prominent, as people now expect to live many years beyond middle age. Health and aging are also being given considerable attention in the study and research of scientific scholars.

QUALITY OF LIFE DEFINED

How one views him- or herself in relation to his or her own personal resources can best define what is meant by the "quality" of life. Motivations expressed by seniors who are interested in raising the quality of life will, to some extent, provide an insight into how others see the relationships between how they feel as a result of their activities and their lives in general. Seniors consider the following factors as essential to the quality of life:

1. Life satisfaction
2. Self-esteem
3. General health and functions
4. Socio-economic status (George & Beardon, 1980).

Retirement counselors have suggested that the basic requirements for independence and quality of life in later years are (a) good health, (b) economic independence, and (c) a meaningful purpose in life to which one attaches significance and value in terms of its social importance.

Asked by the author to rank in order items essential to the quality of life, large numbers of seniors place "good health" in the first position. "Of what good," they asked, "is wealth or improved socioeconomic status without good health to enable one to live life to its fullest?" Indeed, without good health, one loses the initiative and persistence required to pursue projects or programs whose purposes would be meaningful in their lives.

The most frequently expressed concern of seniors is that health problems or disability will interfere with their capacity for independent living. Seniors look upon good health as a status that enables them to be active, to be functional. This includes mobility and an energy level adequate to perform self-maintenance and preferred activities.

Finally, the quality of life includes a perception of well-being (often expressed among the list of motives for swimming), a basic level of contentment or satisfaction, and a general sense of self-worth. All of the indicated factors are, therefore, important considerations in judging quality of life among seniors. Health is an important dimension of life quality and is a resource cherished by a great majority of seniors.

CHARACTERISTICS OF SENIORS

Examining the characteristics of seniors will make it easier to understand the relationships between the changing conditions experienced by persons 55 years of age and over and the influence that being physically active in swimming may have on those characteristics.

The preferred view is to look at aging as a normal process of life and living rather than as one of decline, dysfunction, or disability. This text presents a program designed to improve the physiological, psychological, and general well-being of seniors, thereby enhancing the quality of life.

Considerable research on aging has recently been completed; this should continue in future years. Examining the condition and role of seniors in the United States and throughout the world is of great significance, because

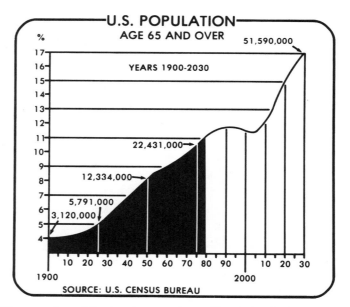

Figure 1.2 The percentage of the American population 65 and older from 1900 to 1975, with predictions for 1980 to 2030.

persons 55 years of age and over will constitute a large minority of the total population in the relatively near future. For example, there are some 23 million Americans over 65 at the present time; it is estimated that by the year 2030 there will be 50 million, or one in five (see Figure 1.2).

Uniqueness and diversity

The degree of uniqueness and diversity among individuals becomes more pronounced as age increases. A person becomes more distinctly himself or herself in the sense that each displays a genetic predisposition and the consequences of experiences cumulated over years of living. Genetic factors set the limits within which the individual adapts to environmental circumstances.

This matter of uniqueness and diversity brings out two important implications for senior swimmers:

1. Because there is a wide range of diversity among seniors, exercise prescriptions and the expected results or responses must vary in accordance with the individual's capability. This approach differs from the management of younger swimmers. Working with large numbers of senior swimmers in a uniform training program would be much less likely to achieve improved performance than would such a program with high school or college swimmers.

2. Seniors require considerable free-dom to adapt to their environments because of the limits imposed by their genetic endowments. There are a variety of levels of adaptation in the physiological, psychological, and sociological areas of functions in life. Individual seniors must therefore be sensitive to the need to make their own adjustments to the environment. They often wish to plan their own programs of work (exercise) and respond to those programs in accordance with the way they feel. Nevertheless, they do seek out direction and guidance as to prescriptive programs for themselves.

We have special interest in recovery from the consequences of environmental demands as one means of adaptation to the environment (life). In chapter 2 the motivations of seniors for swimming are reviewed; these include the self-repair from environmental demands (e.g., relief of tension) and the improvement of physiological function (e.g., improvement of the cardiovascular conditions).

Physiological characteristics

We will investigate the physiological changes that occur in seniors and explore how we can improve these functions through an increase in personal fitness through swimming. This approach promises great potential for increasing physiological efficiency and for raising the level of fitness to a point where seniors can better enjoy life; it has been estimated that even moderate training or practice can set back the deterioration of physiological work capacity by an average of 8 to 9 years (Shephard, 1978).

The studies related to the physiology of aging reveal that human aging is characterized by a constant and gradual decline of physiological function in which the average rate of decline is about 1% per year after 25 to 30 years of age (Heikkinen & Kayhty, 1977).

The decline in the performance of trained men and women Master swimmers 25 to 80 years of age has been revealed in a study by the author. The consistent decrease in performance with increasing age is shown in Figure 1.3. This is consistent with the data on marathon runners, ages 10 to 79, shown in Figure 1.4, which reveals a linear decline in performance starting at about age 30 (Fries & Crapo, 1981). However, there is a great range of variation in functions and in individuals. These variations are often attributed to genetic factors, but there is evidence to show that physiological functions in seniors are susceptible to being positively influenced by a progressive and continuous physical activity program. The physiological functions affected by physical activity are often influenced differently by age, depending on type of exercise, its intensity (how hard one works), duration (how long one lasts), and frequency (how often one is active).

For all of the positive effects that

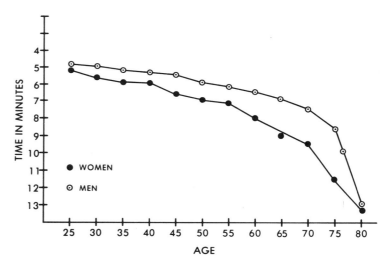

Figure 1.3 The average of the top five times in the 500 yard freestyle, men and women, at the 1984 U.S. Master's National Swimming Championships. The rate of decline in performance is representative of all events for all age groups 25 to 85 years.

exercise may have on improving the physiological functions, there is uncertainty as to whether physical training will counteract, offset, or even delay the *rate* of aging in physically active persons compared with the general population. Nor is it possible to state with certainty that physically active seniors will have a reduced morbidity or mortality rate from degenerative cardiovascular disease. It does appear, however, that endurance training (swimming, in this instance) favorably alters certain factors that are associated with a higher risk of developing cardiovascular disease (Skinner, 1970).

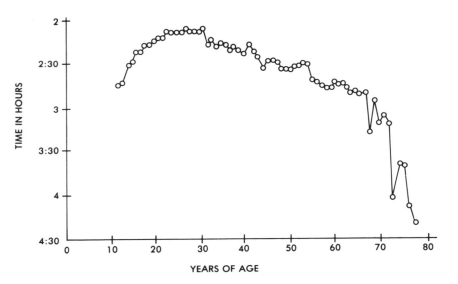

Figure 1.4 World record running marathon performance in men, ages 10 to 79. Curve follows pattern of other markers of aging and parallels swimming performance curve in Figure 3. Performance is maximal from 20 to 30 then declines linearly. *Note.* From *Vitality and aging: Implications of the rectangular curve* (p. 115) by J.F. Fires and L.M. Crapo, 1981, San Francisco: Freeman. Reprinted with permission.

Changes in the physiological systems

The cardiorespiratory system

The specific motivations of senior swimmers as presented in chapter 2 reveal a predominant interest in the need to improve the cardiorespiratory system. The cardiovascular system, principally the heart and blood vessels, is a transport system for delivering blood containing oxygen and nutrients to the cells of the body that require them for life. As the demand for oxygen and nutrients increases because of increased activity of the cells, the cardiorespiratory system works harder to meet these needs.

As the large muscles of the body are used in sustained exercise such as swimming, extra oxygen and nutrients are needed by the muscle cells to respond to the energy demand placed upon them. The waste products of cell metabolism also need to be carried away. These important functions are directed by the heart that must work harder to move the blood through the system. The harder work by the heart raises its rate and pressure, but the amount of blood pumped by the heart is less in seniors than in younger persons. The cardiac output (the amount of blood pumped by the heart with a single contraction, or the amount that can be pumped within a period of 1 minute) is less in the senior than in the younger person, as shown in Figure 1.5. This factor imposes limits on the

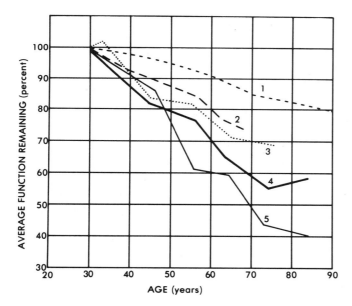

Figure 1.5 Percentage changes with age for five different physiological functions are shown. The average value for each function at age 30 is taken as 100 percent. 1) Basal Metabolic Rate. 2) Work Rate. 3) Cardiac Output (at rest). 4) Vital Capacity of Lungs. 5) Maximum Breathing Capacity. *Note.* From "Theoretical aspects of aging" by N. Shock, 1970. In M. Rockstein (Ed.), *Theoretical Aspects of aging* (p. 128). New York: Academic Press. Reprinted with permission.

adult can increase a cardiac output of 5 liters per minute at rest to 35 liters per minute at the height of exercise (Timiras, 1972). Smith and Serfass (1981) state that the cardiovascular system in older adults (the heart and its vessels that collect and distribute the blood) declines 30% in its ability to deliver blood to the tissues. They also point out an accompanying decline in cardiac muscle size, strength and rapidity of contraction, and a less resilient vascular system more resistant to blood flow.

The lungs also play as important a role as the heart in responding to exercise or work. In Figure 1.6 you can see under maximum oxygen uptake that the amount of oxygen the blood absorbs from the lungs and transports to the tissues decreases substantially with old age. Other decreases in lung function are shown with reference to the amount of air the lungs can hold. For example, the blood of a 20-year-old person takes up, on the average, almost 4 liters of oxygen per minute,

degree of work that seniors can do as compared with younger swimmers.

Thus, the amount of blood pumped by the heart will decrease from 3.75 liters (a liter is slightly more than a quart) per minute per square meter of body surface in 20-year-olds to 2 liters per minute in 90-year-olds. The young

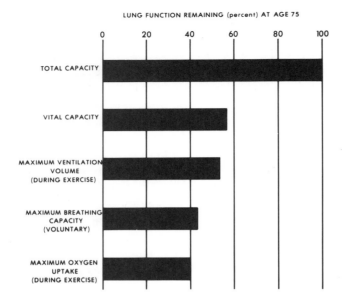

LUNG FUNCTION REMAINING (percent) AT AGE 75

Figure 1.6 Functions of the lung show marked decline with age. Total capacity is the amount of air lungs can hold; it does not decrease. Vital capacity is amount of air forcibly expelled in one breath. Maximum ventilation volume during exercise represents involuntary movement of air. Maximum breathing capacity is the amount of air that can be moved in and out of the lungs voluntarily in 15 seconds. Oxygen uptake is the quantity of oxygen absorbed by the blood from the lungs for transportation to the body cells. *Note.* From "The Physiology of Aging" by N. Shock, 1962, *Scientific American*, **206**, p. 108. Copyright by W.H. Freeman and Company. Reprinted with permission.

the lungs (Shock, 1977). A reduction in cardiac output causes less blood to flow through the lungs, and marked changes in lung capacity also occur. The significant point here is the great difference in two functions of the lungs between youth and older adults. These are the maximum amount of oxygen that can be absorbed from inspired air during exercise and the ability of the lungs to move air in and out.

With age, the bony chest becomes less resilient, and the muscles involved in respiration deteriorate somewhat, so less air can be taken into the lungs during exercise or work. The increased rate of respiration results in a greater resistance to air movement, and fatigue. The overall result is a lowered work capacity of seniors.

Studies show that the maximum breathing capacity declines about 40% between the ages of 20 and 80. The older adult expels about as much air as the younger person does, but the total capacity is less because an equivalent rate of breathing cannot be maintained.

whereas at 75 years of age, the rate is only 1.5 liters per minute. Thus, in order to maintain increased activity, which requires doubling the level of oxygen uptake, the senior must move in excess of 50% more air in and out of

The total functional area of lungs decreases 25% to 30% between the ages of 30 and 70. This reduces the amount of oxygen that can be supplied, and there is less oxygenated blood leaving the lungs (Smith & Gilligan, 1983). The aerobic ability of the senior is adequate at rest, and during mild exercise it is usually insufficient to sustain vigorous exercise.

Muscular strength

There is a 25% to 30% decline to both muscular strength and muscle mass between the ages of 30 and 70 in both men and women (Shock, 1977). Reference to Figure 1.7 provides an example of the consistent decrease in both static (stationary) strength measurements and dynamic (movement) strength in the arms as age increases. DeVries (1977) points out that men's strength decreases at a greater rate after 50, but at age 60 the loss does not usually exceed 20%. However, women's losses are somewhat greater.

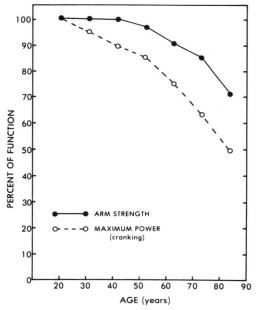

Figure 1.7 Age decrements in muscle strength (•-•) compared with decrements in maximum powers developed in a coordinated movement (cranking) utilizing the same muscle groups (o-o). *Note.* From "Neuromuscular Coordination as a Factor in Age Changes In Muscular Exercise" by N.W. Shock and A.H. Norris, 1970. In D. Brunner and E. Jokl (Eds.), *Physical Activity and Aging* (pp. 92-99). Basel: S. Kargel. Reprinted with permission.

Muscular endurance, that is, the ability to repeatedly perform a specific task (e.g., the swimming stroke) and speed of movement also decrease. Endurance and speed decrease less than strength, relative, of course, to maximum capacity. The loss of muscular strength and endurance, while similar in degree to the loss of cardiovascular functions, is not as pronounced or dramatic (DeVries, 1977). Muscular strength is therefore less significant to seniors in swimming than to the performance of the heart and its auxiliary systems.

Flexibility

Flexibility is the degree of movement in the joint structures of the body. By age 70, a person loses 20% to 30% of his or her flexibility. Changes in the connective tissue in muscles, ligaments, tendons, and joint capsules (including synovial fluid), brought about primarily through disuse, limit the full range of movement. For example, a senior swimmer's strokes will be much less efficient because the range of movement through which they can stroke will be less. A limited range of motion will affect all activities in which seniors engage.

Bone structure

It is estimated that the significant loss of bone, or osteoporosis as it is technically termed, affects at least 15 million people in the United States. While the diameter of the long bones of the body do not change, the inside lining of the bone (cavity) becomes porous because of a decrease of calcified bone tissue and a decreased volume of the total bone matrix.

While men 50 and over lose bone at a rate of about .4% per year, the bone loss in women from age 30 to 50 and thereafter ranges from .75% to 1% per year. After menopause the bone loss increases to 2% to 3% per year. As a result of osteoporosis, many women between 60 and 70 years of age experience hip fractures, vertebral collapses in the lower thoracic and upper lumbar regions of the spine, and overall loss of skeletal firmness (Smith, 1982).

The significance of mentioning bone loss here is that, particularly in women, it is related to lower estrogen level and decreased activity. The possibilities of minimizing bone loss will be discussed in the section on the benefits of exercise or swimming.

Body composition

With advancing years, the senior who lives a physically inactive life is likely to experience extreme changes in body composition. For example, Fryer (1962) stated that the older adult has 25% to 30% less lean body mass, 16% to 20% more total body fat, and 10% to 15% less total body fluid. The increase of body fat and decreased body water increase the stress that is caused by heat intolerance. These limitations must be considered when planning exercise programs for seniors.

Swimming as the mode of activity

Although various activities are available to seniors, many men and women choose swimming as the mode in which to express themselves. Why senior men and women engage in swimming as contrasted to other forms of physical exercise is revealed in their motives or goals. Answers to the question, "Why do you swim?" provide some interesting reasons. How close are the motives of seniors who select swimming for exercise to the most often expressed goals of mature adults, namely, the maintenance of health and the improvement of the quality of life? These motives and their relationship to the activity of swimming will be presented in the next chapter.

2 SENIOR SWIMMERS' MOTIVES AND ANTICIPATED BENEFITS

A knowledge of the motivations of seniors permits (a) a sharing of conditions, experiences, and needs common among persons over 55 years of age; (b) a better understanding of results to be achieved through participation, particularly as they relate to specific physiological, mental, emotional, and social conditions; and (c) the projection of a base upon which to develop classifications of swimmers and prescriptive swimming programs for individuals.

Perhaps the most important facts to be understood through an examination of the motivations of seniors who participate in swimming programs are the following:

1. Each senior is an individual apart from others; each is unique in the combination of background, life-style, interests, concerns, habits, present physical condition, expectations, and personal goals.

2. The motives for swimming are specific to the individual; they encourage seniors to act for their own personal benefit.

3. Motivation, assumed to have a physiological basis, such as improvement of the cardiovascular system, involves the total organism; the mental, emotional, and physical well-being of the individual can benefit from a swimming program.

4. The individual must have latitude to make choices concerning the creative design of his or her program, deciding on how to swim, and upon the frequency, duration, and intensity of the activity.

5. The individual must not only make decisions concerning the degree of involvement but one must also be convinced that the activity is essential in meeting needs, must feel that it satisfies what he or she recognizes as needs, and must wish to demonstrate some freedom of choice in the decision.

6. The relationship between motivation for participation and practice should be based on empirical data rather than hearsay. If swimming within a sensible, prescribed program can yield beneficial results or serve as a preventive measure against the occurrence or recurrence of specific conditions, the prescription should be supported by empirical evidence.

7. The swimming coach of a high school, college, or younger age group Masters' team may be

successful in the use of a team or collective approach; however, a mass approach to prescribing swimming programs is inappropriate and in many instances will not be accepted by seniors. To be successful, a program must be based on the individual differences in physical condition, expectation, and personal goals among the participants.

8. An individual will be motivated only if he or she believes in the prescriptive advice that is given. The senior must understand the basis for the prescription and what swimming can do to improve the individual's condition. The public today has access to information on human physiology and on the general benefits of exercise. Seniors need specific information, in addition, as to the benefits to themselves as individuals, the expected improvement in overall physiological functioning, and in specific functions such as cardio-vascular and respiratory, or muscular strength and endurance. The statement that "I swim to live" is supported by precise knowledge of what the personal conditions are and how swimming as an exercise provides positive benefits. Or "I swim for enjoyment and all other benefits are concomittants" is supported with a precise explanation of these benefits. A physician's advice to "join the Y or the athletic club and take up running or swimming" will not, on a long-term basis, have much beneficial effect, but once the person sincerely believes in the prescription, a positive action based on intrinsic personal motivation is most likely to follow.

9. The extensive personal effort and sacrifice that the older senior must make to adhere to a regularly attended swimming program will not be honored unless the return in self-benefits or self-recognized improvement is apparent and fairly certain. The effort to get to the pool by 6:00 a.m. or 7:00 a.m. or at a later time when the urge to rest seems more compelling requires a strongly motivated self-discipline.

10. Motivation to continue participation without boredom or discouragement requires (a) variety and choices within the prescriptive program of regular swimming to make the program more interesting, and (b) regular evidence or progress. The classifications of senior swimmers and prescriptive programs presented in this text satisfy these conditions. The progress of the swimmer from one classification to another is easily marked, and a variety of stroke or swim techniques is encouraged. Evidence such as a decline in blood pressure, an improvement in respiratory function, an increase in cardiac output, or an increase in muscular strength and flexibility may provide greater reinforcement

in convincing the senior of the benefits of regular swimming experience. The periodic examination of such measurements in a laboratory setting is encouraged. An alternate method is also suggested, yielding a simple, immediate on-site judgment.

11. The motivation of seniors can be supported and reinforced by family and friends. A spouse or children can be most helpful in demonstrating an interest, in offering encouragement, and in sharing experiences. A senior may consider giving up an activity program, but because he or she values the approval of loved ones, will persevere.

GENERAL MOTIVES

Many of the benefits frequently declared by seniors to be achieved through swimming are in the psychological and emotional areas of human factors. For example, seniors often mention the following: physical and mental relaxation (positive characteristics); release of aggressions, which brings about mental relaxation; a lessening of mental tensions, a feeling of mental refreshment after a workout; a greater feeling of confidence after having left their worries and problems behind them, or a realization that their problems are not so immense after all; a sharper sense of alertness resulting in a feeling of improved well-being; the joy of movement or of full and complete expression in the water as a medium that makes this movement possible (e.g., stretching or moving without the hindrance that might occur in lying on the floor or running or walking on a hard surface); a feeling of pride in self-discipline and control of one's actions that are expressly coordinated with one's motives, and to some extent, social recognition or admiration and approval of how one looks ("you are looking so wonderful these days; what are you doing?").

The motives most often expressed by senior swimmers are in the combined psychological-physiological area of human functions. In a survey of 532 senior swimmers of their reasons for participating in swimming, the author found that nearly all reported "an improved feeling of general well-being" after swimming, during which the swimmer experienced 'feeling better, looking better." Relaxation was another motive frequently mentioned, expressed in such phrases as, "provides a release from tensions," "takes my mind off the cares of the day," "is pleasurable," "I enjoy it," "a physical-mental satisfacton," "brings me to the rest of the day with a refreshed attitude toward life and the tasks to be done." Similar expressions are used by active younger swimmers.

SPECIFIC MOTIVES

Specific reasons for participating in swimming in order of frequency were:

1. An improvement in the cardio-

respiratory system with an accompanying reduction in blood pressure and improved muscle tone. Respondents were assumed to have some knowledge of the cardiovascular system.

2. Weight control as a motive for swimming was consistent with an expressed belief that swimming was beneficial in conjunction with quantitative and qualitative control of food intake.
3. Special needs or personal problems for which alleviation was sought included knee and back problems prohibiting running, arthritis, relief from specific pains, and restorative postoperative rehabilitation exercise.

PHYSIOLOGICAL BENEFITS FROM SWIMMING

Water can be considered a medium for specific exercises (as presented in chapter 10) as well as the context for general and specific physiological gains from swimming.

General benefits

From a general perspective, swimming shares with other aerobic activities credit for benefits that accrue. Physiologists, medical scientists, and other researchers generally agree that many of the physiological declines that may occur with aging can be reversed as a result of participating in a carefully designed activity program. More longitudinal studies are needed (research over a period of time on the same groups); nevertheless, there is already evidence that the approximately 1% per year decline in cardiovascular functions that normally occurs can be decelerated through regular, long-term programs of participation and maintenance of training (Pollock, Wilmore, & Fox, 1984).

Fries and Crapo (1981) point out three central postulates of human aging, all supported by extensive studies and experimental observation. First, the maximum life span of an individual is fixed, a fact that is firmly established. Second, many aspects of aging are plastic and most may be modified although always against the limits of a finite life span. Third, the major requirement for the postponement of aging is exercise of the specific faculty. Included in this latter postulate is a need to make a personal effort in

1. physical activity to delay declines in cardiopulmonary and musculoskeletal reserve,
2. dietary and weight control to decrease diseases linked to these factors,
3. moderation of excessive cigarette smoking, alcohol ingestion, and drug usage,
4. active mental problem-solving activity, and
5. intensive social interaction to maintain skills and to provide stimulation necessary for continued individual growth.

Positive results in creating changes in the human organism through exercise (and in this instance to swimming) are linked to the frequency, duration, and intensity with which one engages in an aerobic activity. By making a single decision to engage in the swimming program, the senior may positively influence a large number of physiological variables. Seniors may choose to improve their performance or may choose not to, but if they really want to improve the physiological characteristics of aging and add to the quality of life, they can do so. It becomes a matter of personal choice and personal effort (Fries & Crapo, 1981). Table 2.1 supports this contention.

Physiologists show through their studies that seniors may maintain higher degrees of physiological fitness through the later years into the 80s if they persist in regular physical activity programs, in contrast to those who lead sedentary lives. The participation of men and women aged 80 to 85 in a variety of Masters' athletic competi-

Table 2.1 Modified Aspects of Aging

Aging marker	Personal decision(s) required
Cardiac reserve	Exercise, nonsmoking
Dental decay	Prophylaxis, diet
Glucose tolerance	Weight control, exercise, diet
Intelligence tests	Training, practice
Memory	Training, practice
Osteoporosis	Weight-bearing exercise, diet
Physical endurance	Exercise, weight control
Physical strength	Exercise
Pulmonary reserve	Exercise, nonsmoking
Reaction time	Training, practice
Serum cholesterol	Diet, weight control, exercise
Social ability	Practice
Skin aging	Sun avoidance
Systolic blood pressure	Salt limitation, weight control, exercise

Note. From *Vitality and aging: Implications of the Rectangular Curve* by J.F. Fries and L.M. Crapo, 1981, San Francisco: Freeman. Reprinted with permission.

tions support these data.

One may feel certain that regular participation in the proper kind of physical activity program that is planned or structured for the individual on an individual basis can result in an improvement in the general ability of the body to perform more efficiently, improve overall physical fitness, and improve the quality of life. Physiological studies on seniors have shown that aerobic exercise programs such as swimming on a regular basis under controlled and properly administered conditions may result in lower resting diastolic and systolic blood pressures, lower maximum work pulse and blood lactates while improving cardiovascular and respiratory relationships ($\dot{V}O_2$max). Such programs may also serve as an aid in weight control and decrease many measures of stress. It has been shown that healthy seniors in their 50s who exercise vigorously on a regular basis have a 20% to 30% higher $\dot{V}O_2$max than young, sedentary persons (Heath, Hagberg, Ehsoni, & Holloszy, 1981). Middle-aged and old-Masters athletes who train for competition in middle- and long-distance events have a $\dot{V}O_2$max 50% higher or more above that of ex-athletes of the same age who have stopped training (Pollock, Miller, & Wilmore, 1974).

Information yielded from the Framingham and other studies demonstrates a correlation between decreased physical activity level and cardiovascular mortality and between decreased physical activity and the major risk factors of hypertension, elevated serum cholesterol, and cigarette smoking (Haynes & Feinleib, 1980).

Further research is needed to confirm claims relating exercise to long-term health benefits, particularly its effect on the aging process. Recommendations for major changes for sedentary individuals, especially the inactive elderly, need to be implemented in well-planned and properly administered programs for the individual. The *Swimming For Seniors* program and other similar graded programs have shown beneficial results for the health and general well-being of participants.

Specific benefits

Water offers unique circumstances for human benefits. Many of these benefits are indicated in chapter 10. Briefly, the full movements of swimming engage practically all muscle groups of the body (Åstrand & Rodahl, 1977). Because the specific gravity of the body is not much different from that of water, the weight of the submerged body is reduced to a few pounds, yet the swimmer has the same potential physical resources as out of water. Swimming, for skilled or semiskilled individuals is, therefore, easy to perform at a low level of intensity. Because the body is horizontal, the demands on the physical systems are correspondingly less. Movement in such an environment supports the contention that swimming provides an effective method of training the oxygen transport systems of seniors (Kasch, 1976).

It is difficult to compare the physiological effects of swimming with those of running or other activities because of the specificity of training (i.e., each activity has its own aerobic potential). High oxygen uptakes have been found in trained swimmers, whereas in untrained swimmers they are lower than in runners. The heart rate is significantly lower in maximum swimming as contrasted with maximum running according to Åstrand and Rodahl (1977). The venous blood return is enhanced and the heart rate demand in submaximal exertion is lower.

Swimming movements have been demonstrated to be particularly desirable for seniors with musculoskeletal problems. That is, there are desirable therapeutic effects on conditions found in a variety of physical handicaps. These involve joint pain and limiting disabilities, including lack of mobility. Swimming also offers opportunities to move without injury as may occur in out-of-water programs. There is greater freedom of movement in any directional plane with less trauma than experienced on solid surfaces. Environmental gravity and the effect of body weight on specific joint structures are reduced. Persons who have experienced partial or full loss of one or more limbs find opportunity for physical expression in water.

Flexibility can be affected positively by exercise, and particularly by swimming movements. Studies show that the loss of flexibility in the body joints is caused more by failure to use the joint structures than by normal aging. In normal living one seldom raises the arms above the head. Most of life's routine activities are performed with the arms below the shoulders and seldom are the elbows, wrists, or shoulders stretched. Sitting, standing, and walking do not require any noticeable degree of stretching in the joints of the hips, knees, or ankles, and sitting encourages a flexion or bent angle of the spine with a forward thrust of the head.

One of the primary movements of swimming is stretching or reaching. Efficient kicking in water requires extension of the joints at the ankle, knee, and the hip as well as the spine. The reaching of the arm stroke requires constant extension of the shoulders, elbows and wrists. Efficiency in swimming, as in all physical activities, can be enhanced through joint flexibility. Muscular strength can be developed in senior men and women swimmers through programs designed to improve sprint swimming performance (Costill, 1984). It was earlier indicated that the greatest loss becomes evident after the age of 50. Whatever an individual's strength, participating in any activity requiring the muscles to exert effort contributes to the maintenance of strength at that level. For example, a senior swimmer's efficiency of performance (how great a distance one can cover per stroke, or how fast one can swim a specified distance) may be low because of strength decline. The constant repetition of movement as in the cadence of the swimming stroke applied as force against the water enhances muscular strength.

With increased pressures surrounding the chest of the submerged swimmer at varying depths, the muscles involved with chest expansion upon inhaling may become somewhat strengthened.

Bone loss or bone mineral loss normally caused by aging may be slowed or prevented when one is physically active to the degree that such activity causes definite muscular contractions of the large muscles of the body. Exercise that requires weight bearing (support the weight, such as in jogging or walking) is reported as important in maintaining bone structure or bone growth. The types of physically active occupational jobs or the types of sports that persons practice influence the bone mineral content in proportion to the stress placed on the bone.

Among seniors, it appears that bone mineral maintenance and resistance to fractures (which occur most frequently in women) are dependent to a large degree on the level of physical activity and the stress placed on the bone by the muscles. The amount of stress needed has not yet been determined.

These facts do not imply that swimming is not an activity that can contribute toward prevention of bone loss or osteoporosis. While weight bearing is absent from the immersion of the body in the water, there can be a moderate to high degree of stress placed on the long bones of the legs and arms by increased muscular action in a variety of strokes. The immobilization of the arms, for example, to learn or to strengthen leg kicks may place a great stress upon the leg muscles.

Similarly, the immobilization of the legs to improve arm stroke action stresses the arm muscles. These positions and movements are not possible in other sports or activities.

To reap the physiological benefits from swimming, seniors must participate in appropriately designed programs. In chapter 3 important aspects of individualizing swim programs for seniors will be covered.

3 CLASSIFYING SENIOR SWIMMERS AND PRESCRIBING PROGRAMS

The *Swimming For Seniors* program includes the following parts:

1. Classification of swimmers by ability
2. Prescriptive programs and guidelines for each classification of swimmers
3. Monitoring the effects of swimming performance based on the Affective Fatigue Scale

PRELIMINARY CONSIDERATIONS FOR PARTICIPATING IN THE PROGRAM

1. Seniors should secure clearance from a physician to participate in swimming as an exercise. This procedure will provide relief from uncertainty that might exist concerning any past or present physical problems.
2. The *Swimming For Seniors* program is intended for those who can swim, irrespective of how little. It is not intended for the nonswimmer, nor is it a program for those who wish to train for competition such as the Master's swimmer. The objective of the entering senior should be to swim one pool length, using any stroke or strokes desired. The senior then enters Classification I, the beginning point in the program.
3. Classification for each senior commencing the program is decided by an effort to swim pool lengths without stopping except to turn in a slow, easy manner, using any style of stroke or strokes desired. The stroke or strokes need not be conventional ones. The length of the continuous swim will determine the classification.
4. The senior may decide to start the program after a preliminary period of adjustment or practice. It would be helpful to read first the following sections of this chapter to become knowledgeable about the nature of the program. As with all decisions to be made in the program, the senior will decide when to start based on his or her own judgment and feeling about it.
5. The degree of participation in terms of the length (duration) of a practice period or how often (frequency) the swimmer should practice is to be determined by the

individual. It is suggested, however, that the senior practice at least three times a week for a period of at least 30 minutes in the water each time; the frequency and duration may increase based on the judgment and feeling of the individual senior.

6. The individual senior may maintain his or her own personal records of progress based upon performance levels in the various classifications. Entries on a daily, weekly, and monthly chart should include the amount of yardage covered in a continuous swim (i.e., a single swim without stopping), the total yardage covered in the entire period, and a notation of the feelings of the swimmer during and following the swim. A sample chart is presented at the end of the chapter on page 32 that may be duplicated and posted in a convenient location at home for recording performances. Over a period of time these charts will provide an accurate history or account of progress and development. They will be especially useful in planning future swimming sessions or practices; they also add perspective to the senior's swimming program.

7. As the senior continues to extend the distance and to progress to higher classifications, efforts should be made to improve stroke techniques in accordance with the instructions included in chapters 5 and 9 under each of the five basic strokes and their adaptations.

8. Wherever a rest period is suggested between swimming distances, the senior applies the indices indicated under the Affective Fatigue Scale. The amount of time for resting is a decision of the senior.

CLASSIFICATION OF SENIOR SWIMMERS

A variety of ways have been suggested in which seniors may be classified relative to prescriptive programs of exercise. For example, Smith and Gilligan (1983) arbitrarily divide seniors into two groups: the young-old (55 to 75) and the old-old (older than 75). While convenient, this method is inappropriate for a swimming program because it makes no provision for the broad range of abilities and conditions among seniors.

Physiological status represents a second type of classification. Physiological functions in the body more accurately describe individual capabilities to do work. The monitoring of such measures as work capacity, cardiac output, heart rate, blood pressure, oxygen uptake, and strength are exceedingly important and lend themselves to recording in a clinical setting. Diagnostic measures on single stage, submaximal or a nonsteady state using step climbing, bicycle ergometer riding, or treadmill walking are relegated to the laboratory; they are not practical or convenient to secure in the water or within a time interval significant to the swimmer.

The classification system to be used for the senior swimming program will utilize the swimmer's actual performance. The senior swimmer can be classified according to *starting* swimming ability. The initial classification will be determined by the distance covered in a continuous, slow swim (without stopping except to turn at the pool ends), using any style of stroke. The distance in yards can be compared to the ranges indicated on the classification Table 3.1 (page 22) and Table 3.2 (page 23), with progress to advanced classifications as indicated.*

The advantages of this classification system are as follows:

1. Progress can be measured and interpreted easily. The underlying assumption, in view of the research literature, is that as one progresses in terms of duration, frequency, and intensity of the work load (swimming distance from the point where one starts to the point where increase is made), varying degrees of physiological benefits earlier described will be expected to result.

2. Distinction between men and women is eliminated; thus, all swimmers may be classified on a common base.

3. Flexibility is provided in moving from one classification to another. Progress is clearly indicated in terms of promotions to more advanced classes or stages.

4. The wide range of diverse abilities and physiological capacities of seniors as individuals is recognized. In identifying diversity, the system becomes more individualistic, one of the prime essentials upon which prescriptions within the classifications are based. This approach is more appropriate than a system based on chronological age.

5. The factor of swimming skill, in addition to physiological status and capacities, is stressed. Seniors may be beginners in swimming, that is, able to swim but unable to swim one length of the pool. The subsequent improvement of their basic skills, then, becomes a matter of great importance. Seniors who possess the skills sufficient to swim 200 yd or 400 yd may add to their repertoire of swimming skills while attempting to meet the challenge of moving up to the next higher classification.

6. No chronological limits such as 55 to 59, 60 to 64, 65 to 69, and so on are recognized.

7. The system permits swimmers to compare their performances with those of other seniors in an easy, convenient way and allows a clear

*Diagnostic validity was judged against the criterion of expert swimming instructors' diagnosis of specific skills and of general swimming ability (the relation between identifiable skills and the ability to negotiate distances). Prognostic validity (the establishment of increasing increments in yards between classifications) was based upon the clustering of swimming performances that showed noticeable acceleration after termination of limits within each classification.

perspective of goals to be established by the individual swimmer (see Tables 3.1 & 3.2).

PRELIMINARY CONSIDERATIONS FOR PRESCRIBING EXERCISE

1. The prescriptions, with modifications, are derived from the basic principles of training for aerobic or swimming endurance.
2. The basic concepts underlying prescription of programs are (a) the improvement of swimming skill (application of the three fundamental criteria of good swimming) and (b) the development of swimming endurance through the application of the overload principle and marked by the progression through the 15 classifications (see Figure 3.1).
3. The principal objectives of the prescriptive program are (a) to maintain or raise the level of those physiological characteristics of seniors indicated in chapter 1 with particular attention to the cardiorespiratory system and (b) to assist seniors in realizing their own goals as reflected in personal motivations for swimming (chapter 2).
4. The starting point is represented by the ability to swim 1 pool length. This may be performed with any stroke or combination of strokes or modification of any stroke of the swimmer's choice.
5. The progression to the next classification or the subsequent

Table 3.1 Classification Chart for a 25-yd Pool

Classification	Distance range	Pool lengths	Increments
I	25	1	—
II	25-50	2	25
III	50-75	3	25
IV	75-100	4	25
V	100-150	6	50
VI	150-200	8	50
VII	200-300	12	100
VIII	300-400	16	100
IX	400-500	20	100
X	500-650	26	150
XI	650-800	32	150
XII	800-1,000	40	200
XIII	1,000-1,200	48	200
XIV	1,200-1,400	56	200
XV	1,400-1,760	70+(71)	360

Table 3.2 Classification Chart for a 20-yd Pool

Classification	Distance range	Pool lengths	Increments
I	20	1	—
II	20-40	2	20
III	40-80	4	40
IV	80-120	6	40
V	120-160	8	40
VI	160-200	10	40
VII	200-300	15	100
VIII	300-400	20	100
IX	400-500	25	100
X	500-640	32	140
XI	640-800	40	160
XII	800-1,000	50	200
XIII	1,000-1,200	60	200
XIV	1,200-1,400	70	200
XV	1,400-1,760 (1 mile)	88	360

achievement of successive distance increments will be based on the development of swimming endurance reflected in improved physical condition, and the improvement of stroke(s) and breathing techniques.

6. Progression is aided by the guidelines offered in the prescriptions under each classification and by the instructions provided under each of the five basic strokes.

7. The general prescriptions for progress include (a) exploring the various basic strokes contained in the text, always encouraging creative adaptations; (b) discovering a particular stroke (with modification if desired) with which the senior feels most comfortable and emphasizing that particular stroke; and (c) continuing the refinement of technique with the chosen stroke while continuing to explore improved technique with one or more additional strokes as progress is made to succeeding classifications.

8. The entrance of the senior into Classification X (above 500 yd) will be marked by a change in design of the prescriptions. The emphasis at this point is placed on stroke efficiency and physiological endurance improvement measured or monitored by speed increments for representative distances. This change in the program is expected to add interest and to relieve the monotony of regular swimming routines experienced at the longer swimming distances.

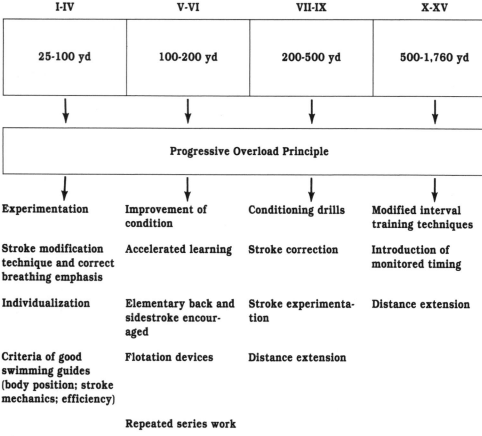

I-IV	V-VI	VII-IX	X-XV
25-100 yd	100-200 yd	200-500 yd	500-1,760 yd

Progressive Overload Principle

Experimentation	Improvement of condition	Conditioning drills	Modified interval training techniques
Stroke modification technique and correct breathing emphasis	Accelerated learning	Stroke correction	Introduction of monitored timing
Individualization	Elementary back and sidestroke encouraged	Stroke experimentation	Distance extension
Criteria of good swimming guides (body position; stroke mechanics; efficiency)	Flotation devices	Distance extension	
	Repeated series work		

Figure 3.1 Conceptual model of classifications and prescriptive programs.

EXERCISE PRESCRIPTIONS FOR EACH CLASSIFICATION

Guidelines in the various classifications of swimming provide assistance with stroke technique (body position, stroke mechanics, stroke efficiency) and general physical condition with progression through subsequent classifications.

Guidelines are offered in four groups of classifications. Classifications I through IV exemplify the beginner who can swim one pool length through 100 yd (distance increments of 25 yd) and are highly individualized. Classifications V and VI apply to those who can swim 100 yd through 200 yd (distance increments of 50 yd), a most significant progression in terms of individual achievement. Classifications VII through IX bring the swimmer to 500 yd (distance increments of 100 yd) and into the significant phase of training for improved physical condition. Classifications X through XV stress endurance, training, refinement of a variety of techniques, and the use of timed performance.

Classifications I—IV

Swimmers in these levels should be aware of the following:

1. Breath holding is discouraged because it results in fatigue. The senior should instead practice good breathing procedures, that is, exhaling and inhaling *completely.* A review of the material presented in chapter 4 on the techniques of proper breathing will be helpful.
2. Use of the hands in sculling by the side is a valuable technique for maintaining good body position when swimming on the back. (Refer to chapter 5, Preliminary Considerations.)
3. Beginning swimmers should review the elementary backstroke and sidestroke sections of the text to determine which stroke is more comfortable. Most beginners prefer one of these two strokes.
4. It is extremely important for swimmers to experiment with a variety of ways to swim using modifications of standard strokes if desired (chapters 5, 6, and 7, especially). The objective should be to discover a preferred style of swimming that may be used for moving into the next higher classification. Provide time in the daily workout to practice the techniques of another stroke as well.
5. At the beginning of each swim session, following an adequate warm-up or adjustment period, the senior should swim the best distance from the previous session and attempt to extend the distance.
6. It is preferable to spend a longer period of time in learning a stroke or modified stroke technique and performing it correctly and easily in order to make progress than to make an intensive effort to struggle through the distance. Achieving the distance increment will be a natural result of good stroke mechanics and good breathing technique.
7. Swimmers should be encouraged to use a flotation device while swimming the pool length(s) to help maintain good body position and to permit the swimmer to concentrate on the mechanics of the stroke. (Refer to chapter 5, Preliminary Considerations—Flotation Device.) Once the three criteria of good swimming are achieved (body position, stroke mechanics, general efficiency) the device may be set aside.

Classifications V & VI

1. The distance goal is 200 yd, which can be significant in raising the level of physiological conditioning and accelerating learning. The swimmer should not struggle to reach the goal; instead the goal

should be achieved by consistent application of the three criteria of good swimming and by the overload principle.

2. Upon completion of the 100-yd distance, and without stopping, the swimmer should attempt to swim a slightly longer distance, perhaps an additional 20 ft. Note the distance beyond the 100 yd. This effort should be performed only once within a single swim session.

3. After sufficient rest following the distance of 100 yd plus, the swimmer should complete three or four 50-yd swims, resting after each one.

4. At each succeeding attendance session or workout, the process in #2 should be repeated with an effort to extend the distance beyond the previous session. After sufficient rest, the swimmer should complete the series of 50-yd swims as indicated in #3.

5. The swimmer should always practice and be conscious of good body position, correct stroke mechanics, and as much as possible, the gliding phase following propulsion, which indicates efficiency.

6. The swimmer should not attempt to swim exclusively on his or her back. The swimmer may be efficient in elementary backstroke swimming, but this ability to the exclusion of other skills does not provide an assurance of safety.

7. The swimmer should schedule time after the distance swim to engage in individual practice of stroke techniques and breath control. The swimmer should continue practicing to perfect his or her favorite stroke, and also continue to experiment with another choice of stroke or modification of stroke as presented in the text.

Classifications VII—IX

1. Progress becomes marked after a long period of conditioning drills, stroke correction, and new stroke experimentation. The chief characteristic of this period is the emphasis on the "overload" session. Once a week, or one in every three practice sessions, the swimmer is to extend him- or herself beyond the limits of the last recorded swimming distance (anywhere between 200 and 500 yd).

2. In each of the sessions between the overload session (extension beyond earlier limit), the swimmer should schedule at least one but preferably two 200-yd leisurely swims uninterrupted but with a rest of 5 to 10 minutes following each.

3. In all sessions whether the overload session as indicated in #1 or the normal load sessions as in #2, the swimmer should finish the periods with a series of three 50-yd easy swims providing adequate rest following each. The Affective Fatigue scale (pp. 29-31) may be used to monitor performance.

4. At least one half of each practice session should be devoted to leisurely practice on stroke techniques and breath control skills. Referring to sections of the text related to these topics will be helpful. The swimmer should consider immobilization of legs or arms: kicking while holding on to the pool wall or with a kick board in open water across the pool width, and arm stroking with a styrofoam buoy between the legs or other device (consult Stroke sections on these points).

5. A model practice session is suggested, but the individual senior will always want to plan his or her own sessions, varying the content from session to session. For example:

   • Take a few minutes to adjust or warm-up in the water (kicking practice holding on pool wall, pushing off wall, and gliding and stretching; hand-sculling in vertical position, stroking).

   • Commence the distance swim or swims (#1 or #2) in a leisurely manner with a particular stroke or combination of strokes, preferably not more than 50% of the distance on the back. Concentrate on the three criteria of good swimming.

   • After a sufficient period of rest (Affective Fatigue Scale) finish the pool-length swims with the 50-yd swims as indicated in #3. If your condition permits, increase the pace of the 50 yd swims a bit above that used in the distance swims, always maintaining good body position and good stroke mechanics.

   • Complete the practice sessions with a review and practice of stroke techniques across the pool width, if possible, or the single pool length as indicated in #4.

Classifications X—XV

1. When the swimmer has reached the 500-yd distance (see Table 3.3), progress through the remaining classifications should not present the same problems as earlier. The principal objectives are now to achieve the distance increments up to the 1-mile mark. This will be accomplished by (a) placing emphasis on stroke efficiency utilizing a variety of strokes, (b) improving endurance through the application of the overload principle and monitored timed performances for selected distances, and (c) increasing somewhat the length of practice periods.

2. The swimmer is now firmly established in the personally preferred conventional or modified stroke or strokes at a relatively high degree of proficiency. The senior is encouraged to swim with more than one stroke, particularly if the preferred stroke is elementary backstroke.

No more than 50% of the total distance should be swum on the back.

3. Suggested practice periods are presented for the senior swimmers' consideration. Modifications by the senior swimmer should always be made in accordance with his or her feelings on the day or time of practice. The proposed Affective Fatigue Scale should be applied in making decisions related to frequency, intensity, and duration of practice.

4. The model practice periods represent suggestions only. They are presented in series, the days of the week to be determined by the individual.

5. Practice Period 3 in each schedule shows a monitored time performance at the 200-yd distance, because this distance is adequate to reveal conditioning effects. If the swimmer prefers, a 400-yd or 500-yd swim may be substituted. The time for the swim should be

Table 3.3 Classifications X—XV
Suggested Practice Periods

	Mild (low)	Moderate (middle)	Rigorous (high)
Practice Period 1	500 yd*—leisurely No stops	500 yd*—leisurely No stops—Rest	500 yd*leisurely No stops—rest
		50(40) yd—moderate pace Rest	200 yd—Rest
		50(40) yd—moderate pace	200 yd—Rest
			50(40) yd— increased speed
Practice Period 2	400 yd—leisurely Rest	400 yd—leisurely Rest	250(260) yd— leisurely—Rest
	200 yd—leisurely Rest	300 yd—leisurely Rest	250(260) yd— leisurely—Rest
	50 yd—moderate pace	50 yd—moderate pace	250(260) yd— leisurely—Rest
			100 yd—increased pace—Rest

(Cont.)

Table 3.3 (Cont.)

			100 yd—increased pace
Practice Period 3	200 yd—record the time (refer to description and directions)	200 Yd—record the time (refer to description and directions)	200 yd—record the time—Rest
	200 yd—leisurely—Rest	300 yd—leisurely—Rest	200 yd—record the time (refer to description and directions)—Rest
	200 yd—leisurely—Rest	100 yd—leisurely	
	50 yd—moderate pace	50(40) yd—moderate pace	200 yd—leisurely
Practice Period 4	500 yd*—then, without stopping, extend your swim beyond the 500 yd	500 yd*—then, without stopping, extend your swim beyond the 500 yd	500 yd*—then without stopping, extend your swim beyond the 500 yd
	Record distance toward the 1 mile (1,760 yd)	Record distance toward the 1 mile (1,760 yd)	Record distance toward the 1 mile (1,760 yd)

Note: *As distance increases, change 500 yd to correspond with new distance. Complete all practice periods with self-planned activities. Continue experimentation and practice on variety of stroke techniques.

recorded and kept for reference from week to week.

6. Approach the monitored time performances in a relaxed manner. The recorded time is of importance only to the swimmer. Many pools maintain a large wall clock for monitored swims. If a problem exists, such as poor vision or absence of a clock, assistance from a colleague or pool attendant may be requested.

MONITORING THE EFFECTS OF SWIMMING PERFORMANCES

The purposes of providing a method to monitor the effects of swimming are (a) to serve as a guide to indicate limits or a range within which seniors may extend themselves in order to achieve optimum physiological benefits and (b) to provide a safeguard against extending oneself beyond limits that might be physiologically harmful. The method provided to monitor senior reactions to swimming participation in the program is the Affective Fatigue Scale.

This method is intended for all seniors and is highly recommended for those who, in the initial stages of their swimming programs, must proceed cautiously and with a sensitivity to the immediate physiological effects of physical exertion. The scale is also useful to those who have past or present physical problems and who must proceed within the boundaries of those problems. The method is convenient and has immediate application.

The fundamental controlling element in the Affective Fatigue Scale is *how one feels.* This criterion will be the influential factor in monitoring the degree to which a swimmer will extend him- or herself within the various classifications of swimming. Its use is preferred over other methods because

it recognizes the wide range of differences among seniors and that no one objective standard such as heart rate can be applied with validity to all seniors.

A senior may be advised to exercise "moderately" as a matter of general health prescription or during a convalescence period. But it is difficult to advise on intensity level, or on how much to exercise or to swim. Borg (1978) points out that experiments show subjective perception of effort or exertion (how one feels) is sometimes a better indicator of the degree of physical strain than is the objective heart rate. "Our ability to use perceptual cues to estimate the intensity of physical strain is astonishingly good" (p. 333). The Affective Fatigue Scale is a practical method of determining how much or how hard (intensely) a person should swim.

Senior swimmers find it relatively easy to express their feelings when

they change from a slow, easy, relaxed swim for 5 minutes using an elementary backstroke or sidestroke, to a faster paced swim with a front crawl stroke for the same length of time. Individuals will have developed different capacities to endure intense levels of exertion; a senior swimmer can become sensitive to the effects of swimming exertion and use these feelings to monitor performance.

The senior should monitor feelings at any time during a practice session, particularly during the overload session that is designed to extend the swimmer moderately beyond the individual's normal limits. The following are the determining characteristics:

- general tiredness
- muscular weakness
- feeling of over-exertion
- chest pain
- dyspnea (difficult or labored breathing)

- persistent aches and pains
- dizziness
- unusual restlessness during sleep or insomnia
- persistent fatigue during the day

Experiencing any of these warning signals should result in (a) a slowing down of the swimming pace, or (b) a rest period while remaining in the water and followed by more moderate swimming, or (c) a cessation of swimming for the day.

Reference to age-related training heart rate charts (220 − age × desired percentage of maximum heart rate) is not suggested for seniors in the *Swimming For Seniors* program. There may be variations in maximum heart rates among the elderly with difficulty in predicting working capacities based on $max\dot{V}O_2$ measures (the quantity of oxygen absorbed by the blood from the lungs for transportation to the body cells) and the differing responses between men and women.

The use of a Rate of Perceived Exertion Scale (Borg, 1978) in conjunction with the Affective Fatigue Scale offers some encouragement. However, with increases in age, the heart rate indices on the present RPE Scale need to be lowered at each age decrement. In other words, seniors will rate the degree of exertion higher than will younger or well trained swimmers.

SAMPLE FORM

Classification

Date	Yards Continuous Swim[1]	Yards Single Session[2]	Timed Performance[3]	Comments[4]
8-1-00	150	250		
8-3-00	155	255		Kicked 25 yd on back. Pulled 25 yd on back. Practiced sidestroke.
8-5-00	170	270		
8-7-00	170	270		
8-9-00	180	275		
8-11-00	190	280		
8-13-00	200	285		
8-15-00	200	290	200 yd 7:22	100 yd elem. backstroke. 100 yd sidestroke swam easy— didn't extend myself.
8-17-00				

[1] Number of yards in a single uninterrupted swim.
[2] Total number of yards in a complete practice.
[3] Select a specific distance and time with pool clock or other watch to be recorded for future comparison of progress.
[4] May include record of practice activities and personal feelings.

4 APPLYING BASIC TRAINING PRINCIPLES TO THE SENIOR SWIM PROGRAM

Principles of training related to the improvement of swimming performance, physiological effects, and biomechanical values apply universally to all swimmers at all ages. These principles and their adaptation to the condition and capabilities of the senior swimmer will be presented here. A knowledge of this information is important because the section of the text dealing with the presentation of stroke techniques and prescriptive programs for the various classifications of swimmers will make reference to these principles. The principles will provide a great deal more meaning and significance to swimming as compared with "swimming just to swim," or "swimming only to exercise." These principles will help senior swimmers to relate to their motivations the actual performances or skill in the water. For example, to develop more muscular strength in the arms, the swimmer can practice the correct arm movements in the elementary backstroke, under certain qualifying conditions of force, and develop the desired level of arm strength. This example illustrates the application of a principle to a motivating factor in the swimmer to make participation in swimming more interesting, more relevant, and more meaningful.

Each of the selected principles will be applied to the teaching of swimming strokes and to the prescriptive programs of training or improvement.

WARMING UP

The practice of warming up the body prior to an extended performance is of importance to some senior swimmers. Warming up with some preliminary out-of-water stretching exercises that simulate swimming movements to increase flexibility, and to increase heart rate moderately are physiologically beneficial to the swimmer. Entering the water provides an opportunity to stretch and to gain an increased sensitivity of body surfaces to the water; it also provides a comfortable psychological adjustment to the swimming program for the day.

Warm-up procedure should be a matter of the swimmer's individual design and choice always including an overall stretching warm-up routine.

SPECIFICITY OF EXERCISE

The principle of specificity states that the effects of training are specific to the training medium or mode; improvement is associated primarily with the function being trained. For example, endurance gained in swimming has little transfer to running; the reverse is also true. Marathon runners may have difficulty in swimming only 200 yards. Most seniors engage in a particular physical activity because of personal preferences. The principles of specificity often help in correctly drawing relationships between training for one activity and the effects on other activities.

SPEED OF MOVEMENT AND STRENGTH DEVELOPMENT

The development of muscular strength through swimming depends on the speed of movement through the water of the arms or legs. The swimmer should attempt to increase the speed of kicking to increase leg strength and the speed of arm strokes to increase the strength of the arms. Overloading the muscles by increasing the speed of movement through the water increases the ability to swim faster and is determined directly by swimming-specific upper body strength (Costill, 1984). For example, a senior swimming in Classification I who swims the elementary backstroke slowly may develop more muscular strength in the arms by pulling and/or pushing the arms faster through the correct movement and over a longer range.

TECHNIQUE IMPROVEMENT

Improvement of stroke techniques should be the primary emphasis of seniors in Classifications I and II. As the swimmer becomes more proficient the emphasis should shift to a combination of stroke technique and training for physiological functions such as specific strength, endurance, cardio-respiratory endurance, and flexibility and to less concern for personal safety.

DISTRIBUTING PHYSICAL ENERGY

For seniors in the lower classifications, distributing physical energy over a planned swimming distance should take precedence over intensive training of the cardiovascular and respiratory systems based on physiological stress. This is not to imply that training effects are not occurring in swimmers in Classification I to some degree.

PROPER BREATHING TECHNIQUES

The most important principles are those that relate to functions of the heart and its systems, and of the lungs.

Respiration

Studies show that the amount of air a person can forcibly exhale in one exhalation (vital capacity) is 40% to 50% lower in the average 70-year-old, while residual air is 30% to 50% higher. The total surface area of the lungs decreases by 25% to 30% between 30 and 70 years of age, and blood that leaves the lungs is less oxygenated in older than in younger swimmers (Smith, 1984). The implications for the senior swimmer are as follows:

Exhalation phase of breathing:

Many senior swimmers tend to hold their breath partially while swimming. That is, they do not completely exhale following each successive inhalation. This practice results in the lungs retaining part of the air from the previous inhalation or, over several breathing cycles, a volume of unexchanged air is maintained in the lungs, which causes a reduced volume of oxygen in the blood. Consequently, fatigue develops rapidly and the swimmer must stop swimming in order to rest and recover. The section of the text related to the improvement of stroke mechanics will therefore stress the *exhalation* phase of breathing.

Inhalation phase of breathing:

Increasing respiratory volume (inhaling) is required to facilitate oxygen exchange during exercise. Senior swimmers must breathe more rapidly at the same workload than younger swimmers because of decreased oxygenation per breath and oxygen exchange deficiencies. The senior swimmer should be encouraged to practice breathing fully on each successive swimming stroke, rather than holding the breath for two or three strokes. More frequent inhalation will result in positive results, however, only when accompanied by full exhalation. Full inhalation while swimming provides other positive benefits. Forcible inhalations while the swimmer is immersed in water may increase the flexibility of the rib cage or chest (joints between the sternum or breast bone and the ribs, and between the ribs and the spine). The muscles that are responsible for the upward movement of the chest to assist inhaling may also become stronger through forceful inhalation.

INCREASING FLEXIBILITY

Studies on the degree of movement around joints reveal that, regardless of age, the joints lose flexibility with disuse. Conversely, persons at all ages may achieve or maintain flexibility in the joints through use of those parts. More specifically, one may develop flexibility through a properly designed exercise program that provides specific exercises for increase of joint function. Thus, age alone is not a determining factor except as one limits the use of the body in movements that can develop flexibility.

Flexibility in senior swimmers is especially important for two particular reasons. First, as the senior progresses through the years, joint function and structure change because of decreased use. As seniors decrease their degree of physical activity, the joints tend to stabilize or decrease their range of motion. Knees, ankles, shoulders, elbows, wrists, and hips, which the senior must use during swimming, become more limited in flexing, extending, or rotating. Consequently, the total movements of the parts around the joints are limited, which decreases both the efficiency of movement and the possibilities of producing concomitant benefits to other parts of the body. Second, increased flexibility is important to the senior swimmer because, as expressed in the Newtonian laws of motion, increased efficiency in moving through the water will depend in a large measure upon the application of force in a direction opposite from which efficient movement is desired.

It has been demonstrated that the efficient application of force involves the correct placement of body surface areas to exert force properly. For example, the lifting of the legs from the hips on the front crawl kick or the down beat of the legs on the back crawl requires flexible hip, knee, and ankle joints to expose a larger lower leg surface area in exerting force in a backward direction. The forward extension of the shoulders on the front crawl stroke or the backward extension of the shoulders on the elementary backstroke or back crawl stroke provides greater possibilities for the application of force over a longer distance through which the stroke may occur. The human body is not designed for effective or efficient propulsion through the water as are the organisms that live in the sea. However, an attempt to achieve optimal conditions for propulsion requires the application of force in as effective a manner as is possible. The proper positions of the parts around the various joints to secure more efficient movement will be described in the section of this text that deals with stroke mechanics.

INTENSITY, FREQUENCY, AND DURATION

The explanation of changes that occur in the cardiovascular system (the heart and its vessels that collect and distribute blood) with the progression of age has been presented in the Characteristics of Seniors section in chapter 1. It is important to note here that the condition of the cardiovascular system and its associated respiratory system together represent one of the best indicators of general endurance capability (aerobic capacity). Indeed, failure to maintain it may be the most important factor that limits the senior from performing prolonged work or improving the physical quality of life. The strength and contractility of the heart, its ability to deliver oxygen to the cells, and the quality of the vessels that transport blood are the focus of our attention.

It should be noted that as much as 50% of the physiological decrements that occur with age in these systems are seen in sedentary populations as a result of disuse atrophy (deVries, 1977). The familiar saying, "If you don't use it, you lose it" seems to be appropriate in this regard. Significantly, however, it has been demonstrated that much of the noted decline in these systems can be arrested or reversed through physical activities that are relative to and within the classifications of individuals (Smith, 1984). Although additional research needs to be performed in this area, there is authoritative judgment that positive results can be obtained through regular practice in a carefully planned program for the individual.

Certain conditions, however, must be met to secure optimally improved function of the cardiovascular and respiratory systems. Assuming that the senior engages in a proper program for him or her (refer to chapter 3), the conditions of *frequency* (how often one swims), *intensity* (how demanding or difficult swimming is on the systems), and *duration* (how long one swims during the period of time in the water and over a period of months or years) are of prime importance in cardio-respiratory conditioning. For example, experiments among seniors have shown that when swimming as an exercise takes place less than twice a week (frequency), evokes a heart response of less than 100 to 120 beats per minute (intensity), and extends over a period of only 3 to 7 weeks or only 15 to 20 minutes in a single session (duration), positive changes in physiological functions are negligible or very minimal (Sidney & Shephard, 1978). To achieve positive and beneficial changes in the systems, seniors should swim (a) at least 3 days, but preferably 5 days a week (frequency); (b) over a period of at least 30 to 40 minutes in each single session throughout life (duration); and (c) in a manner demanding enough to evoke a heart response of 60% to 75% of the maximum heart rate reserve or in accordance with the Affective Fatigue Scale indicated in chapter 3 (intensity).

There may be some who raise doubts regarding the feasibility of fulfilling the *duration* condition of the prescription (i.e., extended over the remainder of life). The most successful of adherents at all ages find it most easily attained by incorporating the program into daily life. Students, professional personnel, and seniors place their commitment to a program of participation into their daily routine just as keeping any appointment or staying within a budget of daily distribution of work and study.

Many find the noon hour to be a convenient exercise time, after which lunch and rest may be scheduled.

COOLING DOWN

A cool-down following a swimming session in which seniors extend themselves beyond their normal limits (overload) assists the cardiorespiratory system to return to a condition of normality. Some easy, relaxed swimming following an extended effort or a prolonged swim for distance assists the heart in securing a more normal distribution of blood throughout the body. The overall general feeling following a cool-down period of about 5 to 8 minutes should be one of recovery and comfort.

TEMPERATURE REGULATION

The maintenance of constant body temperature depends upon a balance between heat production and heat loss. There are degrees of variation in individual senior responses to water temperature depending upon the quantity of body fat that provides insulation and upon the intensity and duration of effort or energy expended during swimming. In other words, heat balance in cool or cold temperatures can best be achieved by increased heat production through continuous swimming rather than immersion with little vigorous movement.

Based upon a consensus of seniors, immersion in water less than 74°F (23.3°C) constitutes cold stress. Increased vasodilation of the peripheral cells of the body occurring from extended effort in warmer-than-normal water temperature results in undue fatigue and in greater than normal demands on the cardiovascular system as well as creating an innervating effect. The most desirable ranges of swimming pool water temperatures for normally active seniors would seem to be between 82°F and 84°F (27.7°C to 28.8°C).

The physiological benefits gained from swimming are applicable to *all* who participate in the *Swimming For Seniors* program. The differences assumed to occur between men and women in cardiovascular and body composition changes that occur from endurance swimming are becoming minimized as more women participate and as more evidence becomes available from this increase in participation. Women tend to adapt to endurance-type training or experience in the same manner as men (Pollock, Wilmore, & Fox, 1984).

5 THE ELEMENTARY BACKSTROKE

The starting point for learning the fundamentals of good stroke mechanics is with Classification I. Because Classification I includes only those seniors who can swim at least minimally, the previous chapters are not primarily intended for non-swimmers, although the section of the text dealing with stroke mechanics can be used by non-swimmers. The stroke mechanics are based on sound biomechanical and kinesiological principles; hence, the presentations are applicable to all who wish to swim, from the non-swimmer through the most proficient.

FUNDAMENTAL STROKE MECHANICS

The judgment as to the quality of performance in all five basic strokes will be based on the following criteria:

1. *Body Position.* Efficient application of force in stroking will permit the body to maintain a position as parallel to the surface as possible. Deficiencies in stroke mechanics or in failure to maintain a parallel position are characterized by (a) bending at the hips while lying on the back, (b) keeping the head at too high an angle, and (c) dropping of the lower part of the body, caused by inefficient leg kicking. The primary causes of these defective techniques will be considered in each of the stroke presentations.

2. *Correct Stroke Mechanics* (including breathing). The execution of the stroke movements in accordance with the precise principles of mechanics or kinesiology will contribute, in large measure, to proficiency in swimming. Some variations or adjustments in the applications of these mechanics

may be made with senior swimmers. These will be noted in the presentation of each of the strokes. For example, the full extension of the arms, shoulders, or ankles or rotation in the hips may be moderated by the senior swimmer because of physical limitations.

3. *General Stroke Efficiency.* This term applies to the total stroke during a series of stroke executions. For example, how many strokes using the elementary backstroke, are required to swim one pool width or pool length? Fewer strokes (without taking advantage of an extremely well developed ability to float) indicate a more efficient stroke. If swimming the pool length requires 20 strokes, the individual's performance would be considered more efficient than that of the swimmer who requires 40 strokes in the same distance. The

criteria of stroke efficiency include all the elements essential for capable and proficient swimmers. These include good stroke mechanics, body control, breath control, and efficient application of force in proper sequence.

Keeping in mind these factors that are essential to good swimming technique, we proceed to the first of the five basic strokes.

ADVANTAGES AND DISADVANTAGES OF THE STROKE

The elementary backstroke has a number of distinct advantages for the senior swimmer. Because of these advantages, the elementary backstroke is the first stroke presented. If the senior swimmer is already proficient in this stroke, he or she may proceed to any other preferred stroke described in the text.

The *advantages* of the elementary backstroke are as follows:

1. The face is out of the water during the entire stroke, which eliminates the stress of having to adapt the breathing to a resisting environment.
2. The coordination of the total stroke and the execution of its isolated parts are relatively simple. If a good body position is maintained, the arms and legs work in unison and in the same direction. The stroke movements are easy to practice out of the water and constitute a good out-of-water exercise.
3. The movements of the total stroke lend themselves to a variety of adaptations for individual senior swimmers. Variations in leg kicks or arm strokes are possible without violating the basic mechanical principles.
4. Unlike many other strokes, the elementary backstroke permits a full range of movements that helps to develop flexibility of the joints. Flexibility of the arm, shoulder, and hip joints is helpful in performing other activities.
5. The swimmer has full access to a visual view of the stroke while it is being performed. This advantage permits a greater degree of conscious control of movements related to body position, to correct stroke mechanics, and to general stroke efficiency (the three criteria upon which to judge quality performance in all strokes).

The *disadvantages* of the elementary backstroke include the following:

1. The elementary backstroke, if solely relied upon, offers a poor guarantee for safety in the water. If the swimmer is confronted with the need to change body positions and is not capable of doing so, extreme difficulties may arise.
2. There are some seniors (and for that matter, swimmers at all ages)

who are uncertain or fearful of lying on their backs in the water. Fear is often caused by the uncertainty of being able to regain the standing position when they feel a need or desire to do so. The consequence is tension and a distortion of body position.

3. Those who learn to swim the elementary backstroke proficiently may encounter difficulty when approaching the end or side wall of the pool; extending both arms overhead to grasp the pool trough or edge, they invariably submerge themselves and complete the stroke awkwardly.

PRELIMINARY CONSIDERATIONS

Out-of-water practice

The elementary backstroke lends itself to out-of-water practice, which helps to reinforce the correct movements in proper sequence. Because the swimmer lies on his or her back, the movements are in full view and are easy to check and correct. The stroke movements may be practiced lying flat on the floor with the head raised high enough to view the legs and arms. The swimmer can follow the same sequence of movements as presented in the in-water training, that is, leg movements (except the whip kick, which cannot be practiced on the floor), arm movements, and total stroke.

Hand sculling

A technique for supporting the body on the surface or, if in a vertical position, supporting the head above the surface is called hand sculling. Hand sculling may be used for a variety of purposes involving body changes while in the water. It is applied for self-support in order to improve *body position*, one of the primary criteria for judging quality performance. Hand sculling can assist in maintaining the body in a horizontal position while floating, gliding, or practicing the kick while on the back. Because maintenance of good body position is especially important, hand sculling, simple as it is, is also of great importance.

To practice sculling, stand in waist-deep water and place both hands on the water surface in front of you—palms down, 12 in. apart, and fingers together. With the arms relaxed and bent at the elbow, turn the palms of the hands slightly outward about 30° (with the thumbs in a downward position). Press the hands outward about 12 in. Then rotate or turn the hands inward, about 30° (with the thumbs in an upward position), and press the hands inward a distance of 12 in. or back to the original starting position. Repeat these movements in a slow, continuous rhythm. Keep in mind that the object is to exert a steady pressure in a downward but diagonal direction (based on the inward and outward turning of the wrists) over

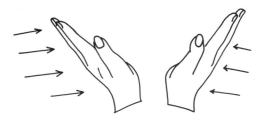

Figure 5.1(a)   Hand placement on sculling

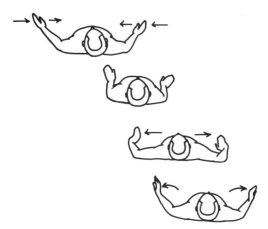

Figure 5.1(b)   Total hand and arm sculling movement

a distance of about 12 in. for each hand (see Figure 5.1a). Then repeat, "As the hands move toward each other, the thumbs are up; as the hands move away from each other, the thumbs are down. Thumbs up; thumbs down."

Place the hands to the sides of the body at hip level. Repeat the movements, exerting constant pressure downward and spread over an area of approximately 18 in. square (see Figure 5.1b). Now squat in the water by bending the knees, allowing the water to cover the shoulders and remain at neck level. With the hands at the side at hip level, practice the sculling movement. While sculling, make an effort to raise both feet off the pool bottom. Attempt, while sculling vigorously, to keep the feet off the bottom for a count of 10 seconds, then 20 seconds (see Figure 5.2).

Some senior swimmers may experience difficulty in the rotation action of the hands because of lack of sufficient flexibility or because of arthritic pain.

Loss of flexibility in the joints of the body is primarily attributed to lack of use (apart from a medical or structural disability); hand sculling in the water can help improve flexibility in the joints.

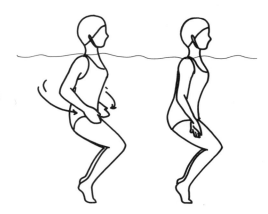

Figure 5.2   Test for effective hand sculling—feet off bottom pool

Body position holding on the pool wall

The correct position for holding on the pool wall, preliminary to pushing off and getting into the correct *body position* for the elementary backstroke, while simple, is of great importance.

To practice the technique of holding on the pool wall, place both hands on the lower lip of the pool gutter or trough about 12 in. apart. Place both feet against the wall at a depth of about 20 in. If the feet are too high or too low, the swimmer may push off into an undesirable body position. Place the bent knees between the extended arms with the thighs, legs, and feet together, and with the back of the head just touching the water surface (see Figure 5.3). If the head is in an upward and forward position, there will be a tendency to enter a partially flexed body position on the pushoff. If the head is in a more extreme backward position, there will be a tendency

Figure 5.3 Head and body position on push off wall

for the head and face to go under water on the pushoff.

Breathing

Unlike the breathing technique applied on the front crawl stroke, breathing during the swimming of the elementary backstroke does not necessarily have to be controlled or arbitrarily placed within a precise rhythm of the total stroke or in synchronization with the arm stroke. It is true that there is a logical breathing pattern for stroke swimming such as the elementary backstroke. The logic would be to inhale when the body buoyancy is least

and to exhale when buoyancy is greatest. However, rather than a controlled method of breathing for the elementary backstroke, it is suggested that senior swimmers breathe independently of stroke action. It is very important that the swimmer seek to inhale fully and to exhale fully, with emphasis, as with all stroking, on the *exhalation* phase of the breathing cycle. The intent is to reduce as much as possible the residual air contained in the lungs so that on inhalation a greater exchange of air may result.

Regaining a standing position from floating or gliding

This is an extremely important skill to be learned for those who possess high buoyancy and have difficulty in changing body positions from lying on their backs in a horizontal position to a standing or vertical position. The uncertainty of regaining a standing position often impedes any further progress in learning to swim on the back. The technique for regaining a standing position is as follows:

1. Forcefully raise the head and extend it *forward* as far as possible.
2. Bend at the waist so as to approximate a sitting position. These two actions, thrusting the head forward and bending at the waist, will tend to force the legs or feet downward.
3. Bend (flex) the knees into a tuck position. Bending at the waist and the knee flexion can be performed at the same time.
4. With both arms still in the position of full extension (as on the glide), turn the palms *outward* and forcefully pull outward and diagonally downward (see Figure 5.4 a-d).

The pulling action (such as on a modified arm breaststroke action) will cause the head and upper body to move forward over the hips and feet. As this action occurs, the feet may now be placed on the pool bottom. It may be necessary in the practice or learning stages to execute more than one arm stroke backward so as to move the upper body forward over the legs and feet.

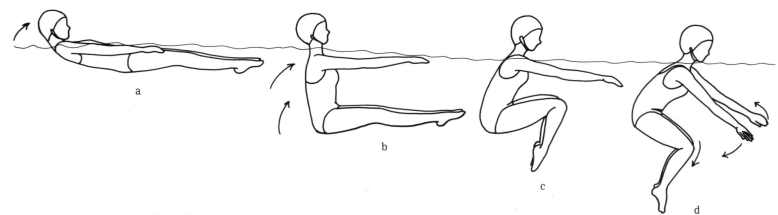

Figure 5.4 Regaining standing position: (a) raise head; (b) bend at waist; (c) bend knees; (d) pull out, down, and back

Use of flotation devices while learning

The purpose of a flotation device is to maintain a proper body position while practicing the arm movements. The swimmer can more easily concentrate upon the hand sculling while in the back-lying position or on the armstroke in the elementary backstroke. A device that can be strapped to the waist (Silvia, 1970) or a styrofoam cylindrical-shaped twin buoy (see Figures 5.5 a and b) is most commonly used. The flotation device should be close to the body's center of gravity to achieve an equal balancing of total

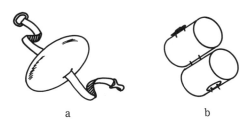

Figure 5.5(a)(b) Typical flotation devices: (a) Silvia egg; (b) styrofoam twin buoy

body weight. The styrofoam or other similar devices best fit between the legs as close to the hips as possible. (Refer to Figures 5.6 a and b.)

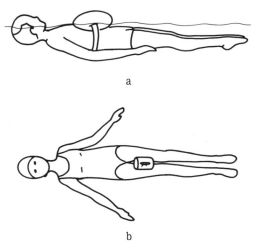

Figure 5.6(a)(b) Positioning of flotation devices: (a) Silvia egg; (b) twin buoy

BACKSTROKE TECHNIQUES AND PROGRESSIONS

Push off pool wall and glide, arms by side

The objective of this skill is to achieve the correct *body position* for the elementary backstroke and for other backstrokes. Taking the correct position of holding on the wall (see Figure 5.3), gently drop the hands off the wall, allowing the arms to rest by your sides during the glide. As you gently push backward, slowly raise the hips until the body is parallel to the surface of the water (see Figure 5.7). Place the head back but not far enough to permit the water to flow over the face during the pushoff. Some adjustment

Figure 5.7 Back gliding body position

in the head position may be necessary to (a) prevent water from flowing over the face and (b) prevent dropping of the hips (if the head is raised too high and too forward). A general guide is to keep the back of the head in the water to a point where the surface line covers the ears. Again, some seniors may possess a high degree of buoyancy, permitting a higher head position.

The back glide position with the arms held loosely by the sides is maintained until backward momentum is lost and the legs begin to sink. A technique for regaining the upright standing position from lying on the back has been presented in the foregoing section of Preliminary Considerations for seniors who have high buoyancy and whose feet do not sink to the pool bottom.

Push off pool wall and glide, arms by sides and hand scull

The objective of this skill is to maintain a good *body position* while on the back by adding the skill of hand sculling. Review the hand sculling skill at this point (see Preliminary Considerations). Hand sculling should allow the body to maintain a position that will considerably enhance elementary backstroke swimming. As the swimmer practices, he or she may be able to use hand sculling to swim backward. This movement is attained simply by exerting any degree of pressure or force with the hands toward the feet or legs without neglecting the original intent of hand sculling. Hand sculling is also an excellent exercise for development of strength and endurance in the arms and shoulders.

The senior swimmer may find it to be helpful at this point to utilize a flotation device placed between the legs or around the waist. (Refer to use of flotation devices under Preliminary Considerations.) This technique is particularly recommended should the swimmer experience difficulty in maintaining the legs in a position parallel to the water surface. Again, as in the introduction of the correct methods of swimming, correct *body position* should be secured prior to subsequent progressions. Once the correct technique of gliding and hand sculling has been mastered, the swimmer should abandon the use of the flotation device and perform the stroke as prescribed.

The leg kick for elementary backstroke

The technique and style of kicking that senior swimmers must learn for the elementary backstroke will include both the conventional type kicks and variants. Swimmers should (a) know what constitutes correct technique for the various strokes and (b) apply the techniques in the most efficient manner. Some adjustments in conventional techniques may be required. These adjustments are to be encouraged and will, to a large extent, be decided upon by the senior him- or herself. Some suggestions for adjustments will be made as the techniques are presented.

The whip kick

Observations, discussions, and working experience have revealed that the whip kick is not always suitable for senior swimmers without adjustment. If the whip kick is unsuitable, attention and effort should be turned to another style of kicking. Instructions are as follows:

Step 1. Standing in shallow water (up to the waist), place the back against the pool wall. Place hands over the shoulders and grasp the edge of the pool gutter (trough). Keeping the upper back in contact with the wall and holding firmly with the hands, raise both legs and hips upward to the surface of the water. The body should now be extended just under and parallel with the water surface. The legs and hips are now in full view of the swimmer and are ready to perform the first movement of the kick (see Figure 5.8 a).

It may be that the swimmer will experience some difficulty in achieving the described position due to lack of muscular strength in the abdominal muscles, arms, and shoulders. Practice with this skill may constitute in itself a desirable form of exercise for strength development and is to be encouraged. The performance of the exercise in the water is an advantage because of body buoyancy.

Step 2. With thighs parallel with the water surface, in normal position in relation to the hips, drop the lower legs downward toward the pool bottom (lower the heels). The legs now resemble an inverted L-shape so as to look like ⌐ when viewed from the side. (See Figures 5.8 b and c).

Step 3. Turn the lower legs and feet outward. This rotation occurs principally in the knee joints. The senior swimmer may experience

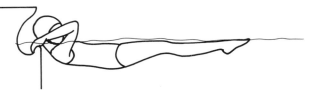

Figure 5.8(a) Holding on pool wall for leg kick practice

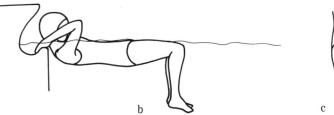

b   c

Figure 5.8(b)(c) Whip kick—position of legs prior to propulsive action

some difficulty in the beginning stages of performing this movement because ankles and knees lack flexibility.

Step 4.   With the lower legs and feet rotated outward, press both lower legs and feet outward into a semicircular and backward motion so as to exert force or pressure in a backward direction. (See Figures 5.8 d-i). Keep in mind the outward rotation of the feet and legs, and the application of force against the water with the surface area of the insides of the feet and lower legs.

The V-shaped kick

The V-shaped kick, while much less mechanically efficient than the previously described whip kick, is much easier for the senior swimmer to perform. Much of the rotating action takes place in the hips rather than in the knees. Instructions are as follows:

Step 1.   Hold on to the pool wall as described for the whip kick practice (see Figure 5.9 a). Starting with the legs held together parallel with the surface of the water, spread both knees out to the sides (see Figure 5.9 b). Do not permit the hips to sink as the knees are spread sideward.

Step 2.   Turn or rotate both feet outward. This is an extremely important movement because it places the inside surfaces of the feet into a position to exert force against the water and in a backward direction.

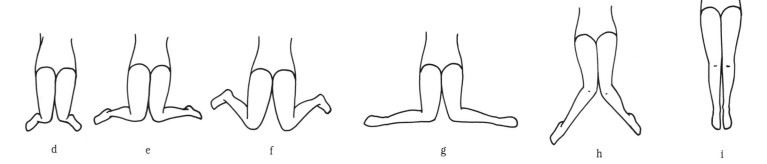

d   e   f   g   h   i

Figure 5.8(d)-(i) Whip kick sequence; (d) feet rotated outward; (c-h) force exerted with circular and backward movement; (i) return to starting position

Step 3. *In one movement,* straighten both legs to form the letter *V.* (The legs should be widely spread and fully extended.) Then draw the extended legs together, returning to the starting position. The senior swimmer must be conscious of exerting force with the inside surface of both legs in a backward direction (see Figures 5.9 c and d).

a

b

c

d

Figure 5.9(a) Holding on pool wall for leg practice; **(b)** V-shaped kick—knees spread; feet rotated outward

Figure 5.9(c)(d) V-shaped kick—one continuous movement: (c) extension sideward; (d) forceful adduction

Kicking practice for elementary backstroke

There are four parts to this drill for kicking practice. Holding the wall in the starting position described in Preliminary Considerations: (a) push gently, dropping the arms to the side, lifting the hips upward easily to get into the proper body position; (b) glide backward keeping the entire body parallel to the water surface; (c) scull with the hands by the side as described for maintaining good body position; and (d) practice the chosen kick. The choice of kick may be made from whip kick, V-shaped kick or adaptation. The use of a flotation device as described may be desired. (See Preliminary Considerations.) The swimmer must be especially conscious of doing the following:

1. Maintaining the correct body position at all times. Hand sculling will assist.

2. Completing each kick before starting another, regardless of the kick selected.

3. Always returning to the correct body position (or gliding position) before starting another kick.
4. Continuing the complete drill across the pool width or length.

The arm stroke on the elementary backstroke

Two types of arm positions are suggested. Directions for the *T-stroke* and the *V-stroke* are as follows:

The T-stroke

1. In shallow water, lie on the back, arms by the sides, in a position parallel to the water surface, or if the heels rest on the pool bottom, in an inclined position. Extend the head backward as in the normal stroking position. Use a flotation device to maintain the correct body position if necessary. (Refer to flotation device use in Preliminary Considerations.)

2. Keeping the fingers in light contact with the *sides* of the body and under water, draw the hands upward toward and just above the hips. Then drop the elbows downward.
3. With the fingers leading the way, reach outward to a T-position fully extending both arms. (See Figures 5.10 a-e). Keep the arms under water at all times.
4. From the fully extended T-position, turn the palms of the hands toward the feet so that the thumbs are closest to the water surface.
5. Exert force in a backward direction by pressing or pushing the hands toward the feet, keeping the arms fully extended, until the arms return to the sides to the starting position. The direction of push is parallel to the water surface and at about 4 to 6 in. deep. (See Figures 5.10 a-g).
6. Check the body position at this point before starting another arm stroke. Resort to hand sculling if

necessary to regain good body position.

The V-stroke

1. Assume the starting position as presented in Step 1 of the T-stroke.
2. Draw the hands sideward and upward, keeping the fingers in light contact with the sides, all the way to the shoulders as illustrated in Figure 5.10 (c). At this point be careful not to allow the hands to project above the water. Such a position will cause the water to splash in the swimmer's face, cause discomfort, and interfere with breathing.
3. Now drop the elbows downward and extend the arms, with the fingers leading the way, above the level of the shoulders into a V-shape. Be sure to keep the arms and hands underwater during this entire movement) see Figure 5.11).
4. At the point of full extension back-

ward, make an effort to stretch the arms backward as far as possible. The full degree of stretching may be limited by the lack of sufficient shoulder flexibility. This move-ment, however, is excellent for (a) developing shoulder flexibility; (b) raising the center of gravity of the body upward toward the chest, thus providing for better balancing of the body and improved buoyancy; and (c) providing a large range through which force or pressure may be applied over the entire arm stroke, thus securing more distance per stroke.

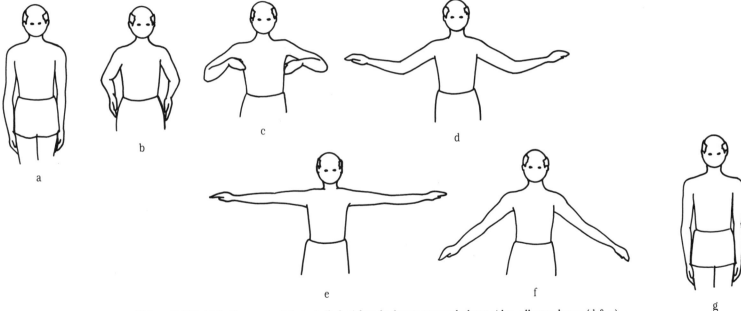

Figure 5.10(a)-(g)   Sequence: (a) start; (b & c) hands drawn upward along sides, elbows down; (d & e) arms extend to T; (f & g) press backward toward feet to start position

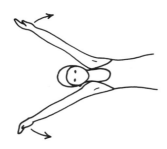

Figure 5.11 Stroke position

5. From the fully extended V-position, place the hands at a position at right angles to the water surface, palms facing toward the feet. Exert force outward, sideward, and backward toward the feet, keeping the arms extended during the stroke. Return the arms to the starting position (fully extended by the sides). The direction of push is parallel to the water surface and under water about 4 to 6 in. deep.

6. Check the body position at this point before starting another stroke. Resort to hand sculling, if

necessary, to regain good body position.

TOTAL COORDINATION OF THE ELEMENTARY BACKSTROKE

The total pattern is as follows:

As the swimmer starts the recovery of the arm (i.e., begins to draw the hands upward toward the hips or shoulders), the legs also commence their recovery. The legs are drawn sideward and spread as in the V-shaped kick (see Figures 5.12 a-e), or the legs are placed into a position to begin the propulsive movement if another kick is used (see Figures 5.12 f-k). Both recovery phases of arms and legs start simultaneously but in a relaxed, slow manner.

At the completion of the recovery phase of the arms and legs, the hands are just above the hips or at shoulder

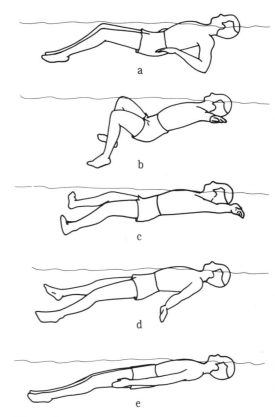

Figure 5.12(a)-(e) Total coordinated elementary backstroke using V-shaped kick

level with the elbows pointed downward. The legs are drawn and in position to exert force in a backward direction. (See Figures 5.12 b and c).

At the same time that the arms begin their propulsive movement back toward the feet, the legs simultaneously kick (press or push) outward and back in the same direction as the arms. Should the swimmer select the T-shaped arm stroke, legs and arms complete their propulsive phase at the same time. Should the V-shaped arm stroke be preferred, the legs will finish the kick before the arms complete their stroke. This imbalance is due to the longer range through which the arms must stroke compared to the T-shaped arm stroke.

The arms and legs then return to the original position as in the gliding or coasting position (legs together, arms extended by the sides) (see Figures 5.12 e and 5.12 k).

Stroke efficiency

As earlier described in the criteria of good swimming technique (body position, stroke mechanics, general efficiency), stroke efficiency is determined by the distance the swimmer travels per stroke. A swimmer who requires only

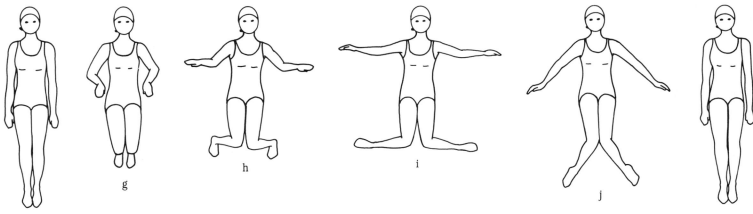

f g h i j k

Figure 5.12(f)-(k) Total coordinated elementary backstroke using whip kick

10 strokes to swim the pool length will be judged as being more efficient than one who requires 20 strokes; thus, the swimmer is able to judge the efficiency of his or her own strokes.

The primary objective in demonstrating stroke efficiency is to hold the gliding position upon the completion of the total stroke in order to gain more distance but not so long a period of time as to lose momentum and good body position. The correct application of good stroke mechanics and good body control is a key factor in efficient movement.

ADAPTATIONS FOR SENIORS

The described whip kick and V-shaped kick are technically correct. However, some senior swimmers may not be able to perform these kicks as described. A compromise may be suggested through the senior's experimentation to develop a kick that is comfortable yet consistent with the basic principles of applying force for movement.

The basic purpose of a modified kick is to maintain good body position and total stroke coordination even though the kick contributes to propulsion only minimally. Thus, propulsion would depend principally or totally on the arm stroke.

Without regard for the exacting mechanics of the whip or V-shaped kicks but with the basic principle of propulsion in mind, the senior swimmer should make an effort to devise a kick in which both legs work simultaneously. There should be some degree of leg spread prior to directing force in a backward direction. The sidestroke leg kick (described in chapter 6, section 2) may be useful. To use the sidestroke kick while lying on the back, the swimmer must turn the hips slightly toward the pool bottom so that they lie in a diagonal or slanted posi-

Figure 5.13 Kick adaptation—sidestroke kick

tion. This position will permit the sidestroke kick to be executed on a lateral plane (see Figure 5.13).

The senior may also find it to be comfortable to direct one leg sideward parallel to the water surface (such as in the V-shaped elementary backstroke kick) while directing the other leg in a downward, then an upward or circular motion. Complete the kick by returning

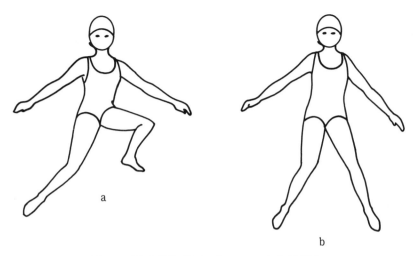

Figure 5.14(a)(b)   Kick adaptation—hybrid kick

to the starting position simultaneously (see Figures 5.14 a and b).

These types of kicks representing adaptations to the conventional elementary backstroke kick do not violate the basic principle of leg propulsion in which maximum force is directed in a backward direction. A review of the backstroke leg kick presented in chapter 8 on Backstroke will be helpful. The alternate leg action in a vertical plane will be most helpful in providing support for the lower body. Any movement of the legs resembling walking up stairs or pedalling a bicycle should be avoided.

6 THE SIDESTROKE

Most senior swimmers in Classifications I through IV will find the sidestroke to be the most often preferred stroke for ease and management in the water. The head is out of the water at all times, thus relieving the swimmer of the problems of breathing adjustments; in addition, the movements of the stroke are quite natural and the opportunity for resting phases are available (sometimes noted as the resting stroke).

The basic body position in sidestroke swimming is one in which the body is fully extended while lying on the side. The lower arm is fully extended forward past the head and the upper arm is fully extended backward along the upper side of the body, the fingers pointing in the direction of the feet. The head is out of the water but lying against the lower arm with its side on the water surface. (See Figures 6.1 a and b.)

PRELIMINARY CONSIDERATIONS

A preferred swimming side

The first consideration, for those who are not certain or for whom sidestroke swimming is a new experience, is the decision on which side to swim. Most persons will prefer one side over the other; it is essential, therefore, to experiment by trying to swim a simu-

Figure 6.1(a)(b)   Basic starting position—sidestroke

lated (imitated) sidestroke on one side and then on the other side. It would be most helpful to observe, before experimenting, a sidestroke swimmer in action so as to observe the total stroke movements. After a few trials on each side, the swimmer may then make a valid judgment as to which side he or she prefers. It is often recommended, however, that swimmers practice on both sides.

Adaptations of stroke technique

As with all presentations on swimming techniques for senior swimmers, adjustments to conventional methods of swimming or the development of adaptations to strokes will be considered. This does not mean an abandonment of the principles that govern correctly performed movements in swimming.

Where adjustments are needed, suggestions are provided concerning possibilities for applying them.

Position on the pool wall

It is somewhat difficult to support the body in a side-lying horizontal position, but with some effort, the swimmer can achieve a suitable position for practice of the kick. The technique is as follows:

After deciding on which side one prefers to swim, the hand of the upper or top arm grasps the pool gutter edge. If one prefers swimming on the left side, the upper or top arm would be the right arm as shown in Figure 6.2.

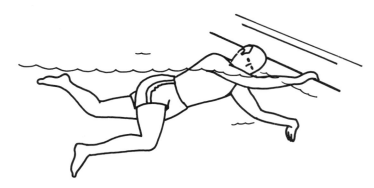

Figure 6.2 Holding on pool wall for leg kick practice

Lying on the side, the hand of the opposite arm is placed on the pool wall rather low on the wall (24 in.), directly under the hand on the gutter edge, with the fingers pointing down toward the pool bottom. With the hands in the proper placement, the swimmer now raises the legs from the standing position to a position parallel with the water surface. Both elbows must be bent to hold this position properly. The correct position is one in which

- The body is on the side, parallel with the water surface;
- the head is out of the water (the swimmer may turn the face toward the legs to observe them); and
- the legs are straight, together (in contact with each other), with toes pointed.

Use of a flotation device

The swimmer may wear a flotation device at any time, whether practicing while holding on to the wall, practicing in open water, or while actually stroke swimming. A flotation device may be of great assistance until the stroke becomes efficient enough to continue without it. It is often inconvenient, uncomfortable, or awkward to wear a device while lying on the side, particularly while swimming sidestroke because of the action of the upper arm. However, a period of experimentation in the use of the device may result in a satisfactory adjustment.

Breathing while swimming sidestroke

As with the elementary backstroke, breathing while swimming sidestroke may be performed independently of the total stroke technique. This does not imply that a pattern of breathing cannot be incorporated into the total stroke. If one applies the principle of inhaling when body buoyancy is least and exhaling when body buoyancy is greatest, one can then inhale on the recovery phase of the stroke (when arms and legs are preparing for the propulsive phase) and exhale following the propulsive phase, during the long gliding action. However, for our purposes, breathing is performed independently and as often as needed and desired.

SIDESTROKE TECHNIQUES

The sidestroke kick

Holding the wall in the side-lying position described under Preliminary Considerations, the practice procedure will be as follows:

1. While lying on the side, the swimmer holds the legs together in a fully extended position, toes pointed. Both knees are bent and brought only slightly forward toward the chest (see Figures 6.3 a and b).

2. One leg is now extended forward and the other leg is extended backward so as to form a V-shaped figure while lying on the side. The swimmer decides which leg is moved forward and which leg is moved backward. The decision should be based upon experimentation or trials to determine which position is most natural, comfortable, and effective. Most sidestroke swimmers prefer to place the top leg forward. At the position of full extension of the legs into the V-shaped figure (a) the legs are fully extended (straight); (b) the legs are widespread, that is the space between them is not too narrow; (c) the legs are kept on adjacent planes, and (d) the ankles are extended (see Figures 6.3 c and d).

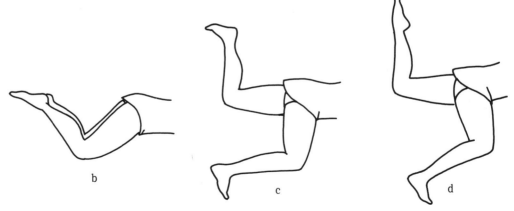

Figure 6.3(a)(b) Initial leg movement in sidestroke

Figure 6.3(c)(d) Widespread legs extension prior to backward push; legs on adjacent planes

3. The legs are now forcibly brought together to the initial starting position (see Figures 6.3 e, f, and g). The swimmer should be conscious of the purpose of this particular movement, which is to apply force or pressure with the surface area of the thighs, legs, and feet as far back as possible in order to secure forward movement. The wider the leg spread on a horizontal plane,

the longer will be the period of application of force. (See Figure 6.3 d).

The practice and development of the sidestroke kick

Out-of-the-water practice

While it is somewhat awkward and uncomfortable, the swimmers may lie on a side or place themselves into a side-sitting position supported by the

arms and hands. A soft pad or folded towel should be placed under the hips. The movements of the sidestroke kick should be practiced.

In-water practice

While holding onto the pool wall in the side-lying position described in Preliminary Considerations, the swimmer may practice the kick. It is suggested that the swimmer slowly practice the kick until tired and then stand and rest. The swimmer should continue to alternate kicking practice and rest periods. Subsequent periods of practice over several days should result in less

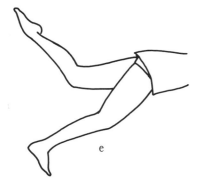
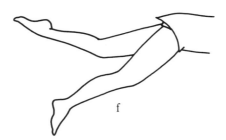

Figure 6.3(e)-(g) Completion of kick—force exerted backward

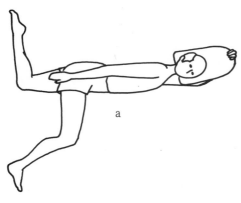

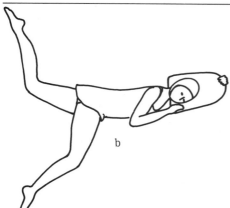

Figure 6.4(a)(b) Two methods of holding board while practicing leg kick

fatigue from holding the pool wall because of improved technique and, to some extent, the development of strength in the arms and shoulders.

Open-water practice

The swimmer may wish, in open-water practice (away from the pool wall), to use a flotation device as described in Preliminary Considerations. Instructions for two different methods of practicing the sidestroke kick in open water are provided as follows:

1. Push off the pool wall on your side, keeping the lower arm extended in front of you, the upper arm extended along your side with fingers pointing toward the feet, and the head touching the water surface (see Figures 6.1 a and b). In this side-lying position, fully extended, execute one complete kick as practiced while holding the wall. If the kick is effective and secures support and forward movement, con-

tinue kicking practice. Remember to fully complete one kick before starting another. Continue kicking across the pool width as practiced.

2. If the swimmer's head tends to sink, a kicking board can be used as follows: Hold on to the wall in the side-lying position preparatory to pushing off. Place the lower arm *under* the board and grasp the front edge of the board by curling the fingers over it. Keep the board in a horizontal position, parallel with the water surface, and rest the head on the upper board surface (as if holding a violin under the chin) (see Figure 6.4 a). Gently push off the wall into the fully extended position on the side with the upper arm (the one that was holding on the wall) fully extended along and on top of the side of the body. If the board slides off to one side, steady it by grasping the board with the other hand just above the lower corner (see Figure 6.4 b). In the side-lying position,

fully extended, execute one complete leg kick as practiced on the wall. If the kick is effective, continue kicking across the pool width. Complete one kick before starting another.

The sidestroke arm stroke

The basic position for sidestroke swimming is described in the introduction to this stroke. Instructions for the arm stroke both in the water and out of the water are as follows:

The lower or forward arm position and stroke

Stand in waist-deep water and bend the knees until the water covers the shoulders. Turn the side of the body in the direction in which you intend to swim. Extend the lower arm in front of you, palm down. Because much of the action of the lower arm is directed toward supporting the head, not much force is directed toward forward propulsion. The motion of the lower arm, therefore, continues pressing in a downward direction, providing support and pushing directly backward to move forward. The compromise movement is expressed as follows:

Exert pressure in a downward, diagonal direction with the palm of the hand, the inside of the forearm, and the upper arm with the elbow bent, until the hand reaches a position level with the chest. The diagonal direction of the armstroke provides both support to the head and some forward propulsion. (See Figure 6.5 a). At the completion of this movement, turn the palm slightly downward and, with the finger tips leading the rest of the arm, extend the hand and arm forward to the starting position (see Figures 6.5 b, c, and d). Do not allow the elbow to lead the arm. Emphasis should be placed on the full extension of the arm. Repeat the arm action a number of times to secure the feelings of support and forward movement. Always complete one arm action before starting another.

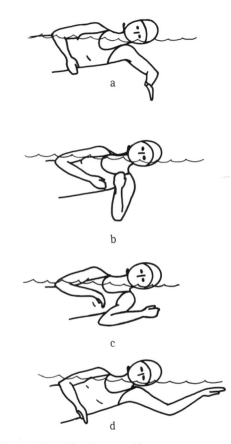

Figure 6.5(a)-(d) Upper and lower arm movements

The upper or back arm position and stroke

Stand in the same position described for in-water practice for the lower arm, and fully extend the upper arm backward so that it is about 3 to 4 in. underwater and parallel with the water surface, with the palm facing upward. This position simulates that of the upper arm as described in the sidestroke basic position. The lower arm may remain extended forward during practice with the upper arm.

Bring the hand of the upper arm toward the chest, elbow bent, with the thumb edge of the hand leading. When the hand reaches the chest level, turn the palm of the hand toward the feet. Apply pressure or force in a vertically straight line toward the feet and back until the arm regains its starting position (see Figures 6.5 a-d). Repeat the arm action a number of times to secure the feeling of forward propulsion by pushing backward. Always complete one arm action before starting another.

The coordinated sidestroke arm movement

Continuing with the same position for in-water practice, fully extend the lower arm forward and the upper arm backward along the side of the body. Lie the head with its side on the water surface and keep both arms about 3 to 4 in. under the water surface. Always return both arms to the extended starting position before starting another stroke.

The sequence of arm movements seen in Figures 6.6 a, b, and c is as follows: As the lower arm pulls downward and backward in a diagonal direction, the upper arm recovers (is brought forward toward the chest). That is, the arms are moved toward each other and to a position in front of the chest. As the lower arm recovers (returns to its starting position), the upper arm pushes backward, also returning to its starting position. Thus the arms start their initial

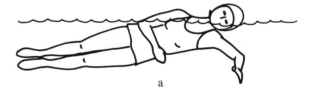

a

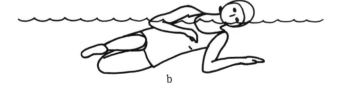

b

Figure 6.6(a)-(c)   Coordinated arm stroke sequence

movement and finish their stroking simultaneously. These movements should provide both support and forward propulsion. (Always complete one full armstroke before starting another.)

TOTAL COORDINATION OF THE SIDESTROKE

The three criteria to apply to the sidestroke as to any totally coordinated stroke are (a) body position, (b) stroke mechanics, and (c) general efficiency. The movements are as follows:

1. The starting or basic body position is fully described in the introductory section of this chapter. The swimmer assumes the starting position for stroking by pushing off the wall in a fully extended position, as earlier described. The body should be in both starting and finishing positions. The swimmer should always return to the basic starting or gliding position on completing a stroke, before starting another stroke.

2. As both arms move simultaneously toward the chest, the legs begin their recovery movement (the knees bend and draw slightly up toward the chest).

3. While the forward arm is recovering (extending forward) and the top arm is pushing backward as shown in Figures 6.7 d-g, the legs are separated laterally (see Figures 6.7 d-e) then drawn forcibly together to exert force in a backward direction. Finally, the body reenters the long gliding position as in starting the stroke. (This sequence of movements is illustrated in the series in Figures 6.7 a-i.)

4. The more effective the leg kick in terms of propulsive power, the greater the forward thrust of the body and the longer the glide; the longer the glide, the more efficient the stroke. Swimmers may find it helpful to remember ''kick and glide'' or ''kick into the gliding position.''

c

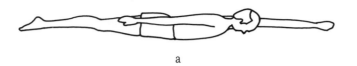

a

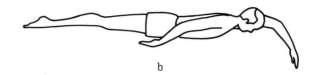

b

e

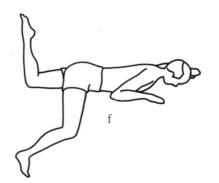

f

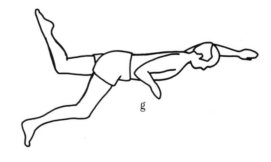

g

Figure 6.7(a)-(i)   Total coordinated sidestroke

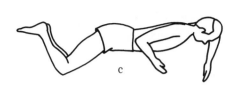

c

d

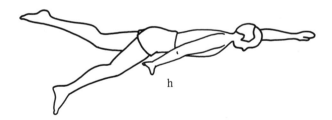

h

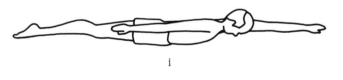

i

ADAPTATIONS FOR SENIORS

Swimmers should not be discouraged if the movements of the sidestroke cannot be performed fully as described. The concern of the senior swimmer in Classifications I through V will be to achieve a sidestroke which

- keeps the head above the water sufficiently so that breathing is not interrupted,
- permits some degree of forward propulsion without concern for speed, and
- permits improvement in the three criteria (body position, stroke mechanics, general efficiency) with continued practice.

The following adaptations, therefore, may be considered:

1. The arm stroke may be considerably shortened. Because support for the head will be the primary objective, the range through which the arms move may occur just in front of and under the chest and head. The swimmer may disregard the fully extended arm action in a forward and backward direction. The arms will stroke continuously with no provision for a glide.
2. The leg action should apply, to some degree, the principle involved in the sidestroke kick. That is, the legs should be separated, then drawn together, exerting force backward with the inside leg surfaces, if only to an abbreviated degree.
3. The described glide and basic body position may be adjusted. The senior may find it comfortable to partially lie on the back. After a period of practice when both endurance and distance may be increased, the swimmer should review the correct techniques and periodically practice them. A flotation device may permit the swimmer to secure an improved body position while concentrating more completely on the detailed arm and leg movements.

7 THE BREASTSTROKE

Most senior swimmers prefer swimming strokes other than the breaststroke; however, the breaststroke does have advantages apart from its use in lifesaving and water safety programs. Advantages to the senior are as follows:

1. The swimmer has the alternative of swimming with the head in or out of the water (both methods are presented here).
2. The body is in a prone position (face down in the water rather than on the side or back) and the swimmer, therefore, experiences a feeling of greater control.
3. When a good degree of general efficiency is achieved, the stroke can be restful and used for swimming long distances.

PRELIMINARY CONSIDERATIONS

Breathing

There are two head positions in which breathing may be performed. The first is with the head held out of the water during the complete stroke. Breathing in this position becomes a matter of little concern because the swimmer may breathe independently of other mechanical aspects of the stroke. If the head is held above water, the arm stroke is primarily a supporting movement with little effect on propulsion.

In the second position, the head is down with the face in the water. At the beginning of each stroke, the swimmer raises the head for a breath. The head is in the water during the gliding position at the completion of the stroke. While in the head-down position during the gliding action, the swimmer must exhale fully underwater in preparation for an inhalation. There should be no hesitation on the exhaling-inhaling sequence. The emphasis should be on complete exhalation. Faulty breathing habits are among the chief causes of fatigue and of difficulty in ability to swim well. The following points should be emphasized during breathing practice:

1. The sequence of inhaling-exhaling may be practiced while standing in shallow water, holding the pool wall gutter. The exercise commonly referred to as "bobbing" should be executed in the following manner: With the body erect, alternately

and slowly bend the knees into a squat, then straighten the legs. As the head begins to submerge, commence exhaling. Continue to exhale on the descent and on the ascent until the head breaks the water surface (see Figure 7.1). As the head emerges, fully inhale, without hesitation. Repeat this exercise a number of times in rhythm, emphasizing exhalation.

2. Two points are important. First, the rhythm of the sequence, while slow, must be steady, without stops or hesitation; and second, the emphasis must be on complete exhalation underwater. It is common for swimmers to hold the breath partially, thus impeding ventilation and provision of an adequate amount of air to the cells that require oxygen for function.

3. Exhalation causes a steady stream of air bubbles to flow over the eye surfaces and may cause slight irritation. Therefore, the swimmer may close the eyes during the bobbing exercise in a vertical position. However, during breaststroke swimming, the eyes can remain open because the bubbles will flow back over the cheeks and neck and cause no problems.

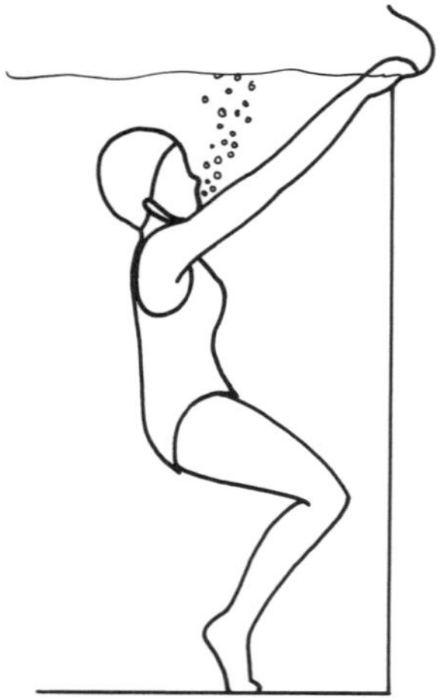

Holding the wall for kicking practice

The following method for practicing the breaststroke kick is helpful: In a standing position facing the pool wall in the shallow end of the pool, grasp the pool gutter edge with one hand. Place the other hand directly below at a depth of about 20 to 24 in., palm against the wall, fingers pointing downward. Lie in a prone position and raise the legs by holding firmly to the gutter edge with the upper hand and firmly bracing the lower hand and arm (see Figure 7.2). The trunk and legs should

Figure 7.1 Bobbing practice—emphasis on exhalation

Figure 7.2 Holding on wall for kicking practice

now be in a horizontal, extended position, with legs together. Should the body veer to one side, adjust the lower hand so it is directly below the upper one. Leg kicking practice may now begin.

Flotation device

As has been indicated in the sections for learning and practice on the previous strokes, using a flotation device may be helpful. Refer to the Preliminary Considerations under Elementary Backstroke and Sidestroke for a review. A flotation device that can be placed around the waist will permit the swimmer to use both arms and legs during practice without interference. Once efficiency of movement has been achieved, the flotation device may be put aside.

Swim goggles

The previous strokes (elementary backstroke and sidestroke) permitted the head to remain out of the water at all times, thus eliminating the need for the eyes to be open under water. Although the head may be elevated during the breaststroke, the head-down position on the glide or coasting phase requires the face to be in the water. The use of swim goggles may prevent irritation to the eyes from chlorinated water and may also make the experience more interesting and pleasant. The style and adjustment of swim goggles is an individual matter. Some guidance may be sought from a swimming instructor or from someone experienced in their style and use.

BREASTSTROKE TECHNIQUES

Body position

The fully prone position is ideal for the conventional style breaststroke. The swimmer lies face down in the water, arms extended overhead and legs fully extended and held together. The body is thus in an elongated (extended) position from fingers to toes at both the start and the finish of the stroke. Whatever movements might exist between these two positions, the swimmer will attempt to return to the starting position. Next, press the arms against the ears to avoid raising or lowering the head too far. The head should remain as it is in a normal standing position in relation to the trunk. Keep the eyes open to facilitate balance and movement (see Figure 7.3 a).

If the head remains out of the water at all times, the swimmer will be unable to maintain the fully extended position. Raising the head causes the legs to sink below the surface to a greater depth than desired; constant arm stroking is required to provide support for the head (see Figure 7.3 b).

The head position used for the breaststroke will determine to a large extent the degree of efficiency of the stroke.

Figure 7.3(a)(b) Body position: (a) head down; (b) head up

The breaststroke kick

Refer to holding the wall for kick practice (see Figure 7.2). The kick practice is similar to that presented for the elementary backstroke. A review of the whip and V-shaped kicks of the elementary backstroke will be helpful.

Whip kick (wall practice)

The whip kick, while most efficient, may cause difficulties for senior swimmers who have not had any previous experience with it. Extreme flexibility in the knees is essential to apply force in an outward and backward direction. To do the whip kick, keep the thighs parallel to each other, and bring the heels upward toward the buttocks. Rotate the feet outward (very important). Keeping the thighs parallel, apply force outward and backward by pushing with the inside surface of the feet (kept in an externally rotated position) and the inside surface of the lower legs. This motion simulates an arc or semicircle. (See Figures 7.4 a-d.) Do not start another kick before fully completing the prior one.

V-shaped kick (wall practice)

This kick is highly recommended for the greatest number of seniors. It is much easier to perform and while less efficient than the whip kick, works well into the coordination of the total stroke. To do the V-shaped kick, start with the legs held together and parallel with the water surface. Widely spread both knees out to the sides. Do *not* draw the knees under the body (see Figure 7.5 a). Be careful not to bend at the hips as the legs are drawn upward and sideward.

Rotate both feet outward (see Figure 7.5 a). In a continuous movement extend both legs out to the sides into the letter *V* and forcefully draw the extended legs together back into the initial position. The object is to exert force in a backward direction with the inside of the feet (which is why the feet are rotated outward) and the inside surface of the lower legs (see Figures 7.5 b and c).

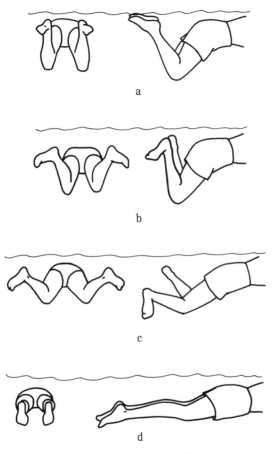

a

b

c

d

Figure 7.4(a)-(d) Whip kick series

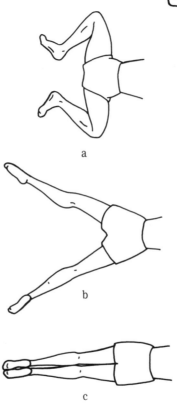

a

b

c

Figure 7.5(a)-(c) V-shaped kick series

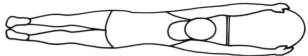

Figure 7.6 Kicking practice position with board

Kicking practice with or without kickboard

Kickboards are available at nearly all swimming pools. To use, place the hands on each side of the board, grasping the edges just below the curvature. Keep both arms extended, with forearms on the top surface of the board (see Figure 7.6). In the prone position, attempt to stretch and streamline the body. Practice kicking each of the leg kicks described in the same manner as holding on the wall. Continual emphasis must be placed on the outward rotation of the feet. The head may be raised during kicking practice, as shown in Figure 7.3 b.

If the legs have a tendency to sink too low beneath the surface, lower the face down into the water. The lowering of the head will assist in bringing the legs to the surface while kicking. To breathe, exhale underwater, lift the head to inhale, and drop the head back into the water. Kicking progress can be measured by the distance the swimmer can kick, legs alone, across the pool width or pool length.

Should the kickboard prove too awkward or should holding it become too strained to use, simply push off the pool wall. In a standing position, extend both arms in front of the body, brace one foot against the wall, put the face in the water, and push. In a prone position, keep head down, eyes open, and practice the kick without the kickboard (see Figure 7.3 a). This type of practice, while very good, may be interrupted if the swimmer must stand up to breathe before the width of the pool is completed.

Arm strokes for the breaststroke

Two types of arm strokes will be considered. The first type, the high-elbow pull, is more frequently demonstrated because it is more efficient. The second type, the head-support armstroke, while not as efficient is more adaptable and is preferred by senior swimmers. Both arm strokes may be practiced (a) out of water, (b) standing in shallow water, and (c) in open water with the legs immobilized through the use of a leg buoy or a flotation device.

The high-elbow pull

To do the high-elbow pull, start with both arms fully extended in front of you and turn the palms outward. Catching the water behind the palms, press the hands slightly outward and then downward and backward maintaining a high-elbow position (see Figure 7.7 a). Your arms at this point somewhat resemble two inverted L-shaped letters ⌐ ⌐ (see Figure 7.7 b). Apply force downward and backward to support the head and to move

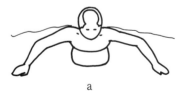

a

b

c

d

Figure 7.7(a)-(f) High-elbow arm stroke action

forward in the water. (Avoid bringing the hands back beyond the shoulder level because support is lost, considerable resistance is offered on the arm recovery movement, and coordination is disrupted.) With the hands in a high-elbow position directly under or slightly in front of the shoulders, start the recovery movement. Bring the hands toward each other with a rounding motion into a position below the chin, then thrust them forward into the starting position (see Figures 7.7 c-f).

Head-support arm stroke

This arm stroke, though not as efficient as the one just described, is excellent for senior swimmers because it provides support for the raised-head position. This stroke may also be practiced out of water, standing in shallow water with arms submerged, or in actual stroking using a flotation device.

To do the head-support arm stroke, with both arms fully extended in front of you, turn the palms outward about 45°. Press both hands and arms outward, slightly downward, and backward. Do not pull backward any farther than the shoulder level. Keep in mind that the primary purpose of this stroke is to provide support for the head with only minimal propulsion forward (see Figures 7.8 a, b, and c). The arm action traces in the water the outline of an inverted heart.

As the arms reach shoulder level, bring the hands together under the chin, elbows drawn toward the sides of the chest; then thrust the arms forward to the fully extended starting position (see Figures 7.8 d-g). The length of time that the arms can remain in the fully extended position before starting another stroke will depend on the forward momentum from the total stroke, principally from a strong kick. The less efficient the stroke, the shorter the glide, and the more often the arms will be required to stroke to maintain support and movement.

Head down position on glide—In the early stages of learning, the swimmer may prefer to keep the head above water at all times. While somewhat inefficient, because the arm movements become almost totally supporting ones, breathing problems are somewhat eliminated. Keeping the head in the water during the gliding action will permit a more efficient stroke. This is performed as follows:

e

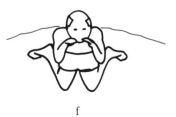

f

As soon as the arm stroke begins, raise the head for a breath (see Figures 7.9 a-d). When the arms reach shoulder-level and start the recovery movement, drop the face into the water. The face remains in the water during the glide and until the next stroke starts its action (see Figures 7.9 e-j). Meanwhile, exhale fully while the face is down, and inhale when you raise the head.

No interruption should occur in the exhalation-inhalation sequence.

TOTAL COORDINATION OF THE BREASTSTROKE

The swimmer may initiate the stroke in one of two ways. One method is as the arms start their stroke, the legs begin to recover (i.e., the movements are performed simultaneously). Raise the head for an inhalation as the arms start to press sideward and downward for the head-support arm stroke or toward the propulsive end of the arm stroke for the elbow high arm stroke (see Figures 7.7 a, b, and c). Then, as the arms begin to recover, the legs exe-

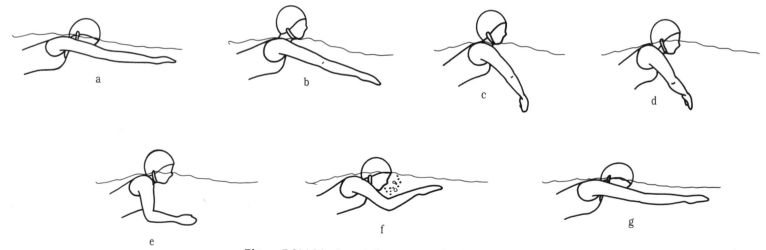

Figure 7.8(a)-(g) Arm stroke sequence—head-up position

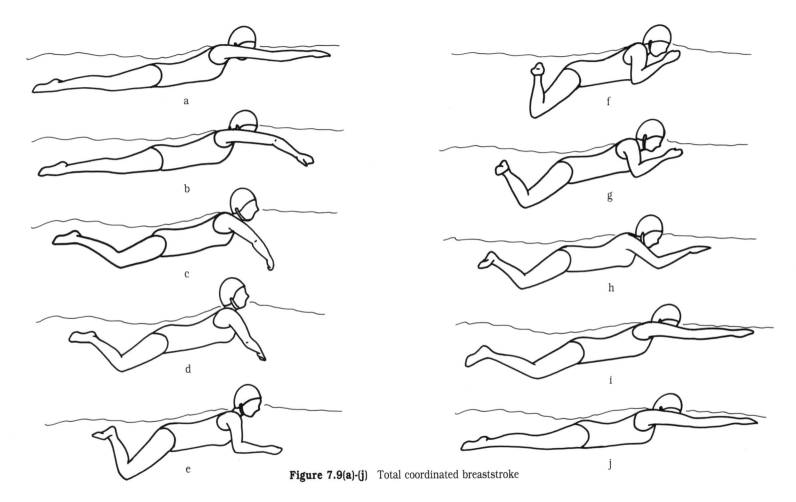

Figure 7.9(a)-(j) Total coordinated breaststroke

cute their propulsive movement with arms and legs completing the stroke together. The long glide follows (see Figure 7.9 f-j). Start another stroke as momentum is lost.

The second way to initiate the stroke is to start the arm stroke first. Once the arm stroke is underway, start the leg recovery movement (see Figures 7.9 b and c). The remainder of the total stroke coordination is the same.

The efficiency of the breaststroke is to be judged as for other strokes, that is, on the basis of the number of strokes it takes to cover a specified distance (rather than on speed as judged by a stopwatch). The questions are, "How long can one hold the gliding position?" and "How far can the body travel during each glide?" Good body position and correct stroke mechanics (i.e., effective movements) with good coordination are essential. The head-out position does not contribute to total efficiency in accordance with the criteria because the length of the glide is reduced. The swimmer sacrifices efficiency for comfort, confidence, and security (assurance of breath control).

ADAPTATIONS FOR SENIORS

As with all stroke prescriptions, adherence to good mechanical principles is desirable. However, some adaptations may be needed. These may be as follows:

1. The leg kick may be a variation of either of the breaststroke kicks indicated (whip kick or V-shaped kick). The swimmer may simply spread the legs and bring them together in the most natural movement for the individual. Some degree of spreading should be incorporated. Or the swimmer may wish to use the sidestroke kick (scissors kick) or some modification of it (see Figures 6.3 a-e).

2. The arm stroke may be modified to provide total support for the head position. However, the arms should not be brought backward any farther than the shoulder level. Or the arms may move in a shortened arc to remain in front of the swimmer's face. (Think of swimming through oil-covered water or through floating debris and apply arm stroke as if to clear a path.)

3. The position may be modified to provide ease in breathing. While using a shortened arm stroke and an adapted leg kick, the swimmer may turn the head to one side as on the sidestroke to prevent water splashing in the face. The long glide may be eliminated and the swimmers may wish to stroke slowly but continually. While more demanding, continual stroking aids in physical conditioning.

8 THE BACK CRAWL STROKE

Although it is predominantly observed in competitive swimming programs, the back crawl stroke is an alternative for those who enjoy swimming on their backs. Because the face is out of water, breathing is performed with ease. The total coordination is relatively simple.

PRELIMINARY CONSIDERATIONS

Holding the pool wall for kicking practice

The method for holding on the pool wall while in the back-lying position is described in Preliminary Considerations, Elementary Backstroke section. Briefly, place the back against the pool wall, both hands over the shoulders, and grasp the pool gutter edge. Raise the hips and legs so the body is parallel with the water surface and in full view.

Breathing

Because the face is out of the water at all times, breathing may be performed independently of the stroke. Some teachers advise controlled rhythmical breathing during which one inhalation (through the mouth) and one exhalation (through the nose and mouth) occur on each full cycle of the arm stroke. The swimmer should experiment with breathing techniques but use the one that is most comfortable, remembering to exhale completely.

Flotation device

A flotation device may be worn about the waist (see Figure 5.5 a) or a styro-foam leg buoy may be placed high up between the thighs (see Figure 5.6 b) to assist in armstroke practice.

Out-of-water flexibility exercises

The arm stroke in the back crawl requires that the arm be fully extended behind or slightly to the outside of the shoulder at the completion of the recovery or the start of the propulsive part of the stroke (see Figure 8.1). It is often difficult for the senior swimmer to achieve the fully extended arm position because of loss of flexibility in the shoulder joints. Out-of-water exercises may help in improving shoulder flexibility. Refer to chapter 11.

The back crawl kick will be more effective if the ankles and knees are flexible. If the legs and feet are correctly

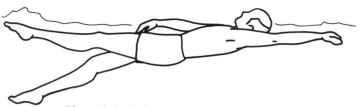

Figure 8.1 Body position and hand placement

Figure 8.2 Bent arm pull at 90°

positioned during kicking, force will be applied to produce movement in the direction desired. Reference to the following section on stroke mechanics will more fully explain this. Increased flexibility in ankles and knees may be achieved through the use of exercises in chapter 11.

BACK CRAWL STROKE TECHNIQUES

Body position

The body should be fully extended and nearly parallel with the water surface, with legs just below the surface. If the back is arched the head will be submerged and water will flow over the face. Allowing the hips to flex will cause them to sag and the legs to drop too low. The head should be carried normally with the chin slightly down toward the chest without changing position so the feet can be seen. Normally, the back of the head and ears are underwater (see Figure 8.1). The body is not expected to maintain the same position at all times. Rather, the body rolls on a longitudinal axis during the arm stroking (refer to the following arm stroke description).

The arm stroke

Many senior swimmers have difficulty with the back crawl arm stroke because shoulder pain and loss of flexibility may severely limit rotation and extension of the shoulder. The following five aspects of the back crawl arm stroke will be considered: arm and hand placement, propulsive action (arm action during pulling and pushing), arm recovery, body roll related to arm stroke, and head position in relation to the arms.

Arm and hand placement

The arms are used alternately in the back crawl. The stroking arm starts the back crawl arm stroke straight, in

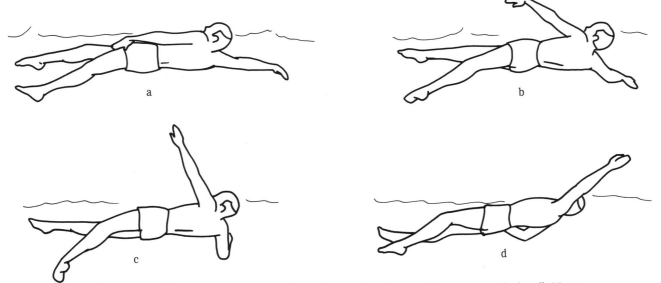

Figure 8.3(a)-(d) Backstroke sequence: (a) relative position of arms; (b) bent arm and body roll; (c) arm recovery; (d) hand placement

the water behind and slightly outside the shoulder. The other arm is straight, beside the body. Rotate the stroking arm so the palm faces outward, allowing the little finger to enter the water first (see Figures 8.1 and 8.3 a) such as in a karate-chop position. This hand position is a specific place-ment action, that is, not forcibly thrown or flung into the water.

Propulsive action

The stroking action begins with the arm straight, hand behind and slightly outside the shoulder, and 6 in. below the surface. Pull down and press out-ward (as in a combination down-sweeping action and outward pressing movement), bending the elbow for propulsive efficiency; allow the body to roll slightly toward the stroking arm (see Figures 8.3 a and b). The hand will move from 15 in. at the initial stage to a depth of about 6 to 8 in.

halfway through the stroke (90° angle flexing of the elbow) as in Figure 8.4. As the arm completes its pushing movement through to the thigh, extend the elbow so the arm is straight as the hand pushes downward. Turn the palm inward to enter the recovery phase with the least resistance (see Figure 8.4). If the elbow leads the hand in the middle of the propulsive phase, the hand and arm will lose their effectiveness during the bent-elbow position. This negates the primary purpose of the propulsive phase, which is to exert force efficiently in a direction opposite from which movement is desired.

Arm recovery

As the hand completes its final propulsive movement by the side of the thigh, the recovery action starts. Raise the shoulder slightly, rolling the body to the opposite side. Lift the straight arm and swing it backward to the arm and hand placement position shown in Figures 8.3 a and b.

Figure 8.4 Pattern of bent arm stroke

During the lifting and swinging motion, keep the hand, wrist, and arm straight but relaxed. As the hand passes overhead, the palm rotates outward. During the recovery do not swing the arm to the side but rather directly overhead as you reach for the entry position.

Body roll related to the arm stroke

Body roll assists in two positions during the arm stroke: when lowering the arm and hand to a depth of about 15 in. to begin propulsion, and when the arm has completed its propulsive action and the raising of the shoulder commences the hand lift or recovery. Hand entry and submersion on one side of the body and start of the recovery movement on the opposite side of the

body occur simultaneously (see Figures 8.3 a-d).

Head position in relation to the arms

Two different head positions may be used during stroking. In the first, the back of the head and ears are submerged and the eyes are focused upward or toward the feet. The second position is for the more efficient swimmer, in which the head is raised slightly, with the water line just below the ears. The chin is closer to the chest and the eyes are focused toward the feet. The head-back position better aids the senior swimmer in arm and shoulder extension on arm and hand placement (see Figures 8.1 and 8.2) because holding the head too high or forward interferes with using the arms and hands in an easy, relaxed manner; holding the head too far forward may cause the hips to sag.

The kick

The correct positioning of the leg (with emphasis on the knee joint) and the foot (with emphasis on the ankle) will improve the back crawl kick. The legs are kept close together, kicking up and down alternately to a depth of 14 to 18 in. The principal source of muscular power comes from the large muscles of the hips and thighs. The positioning of the legs can be better understood by viewing the action of each. Positions may be divided into the downbeat and the upbeat of the leg.

The downbeat of the leg

When the leg reaches its highest position on the upbeat and is ready to start down, the leg is fully extended, knee straight, and foot extended (see Figure 8.5 a). This fully extended position at the height of the upbeat is exceptionally important because maximum force is directed by exposing as much as possible the lower surface areas of the thigh, the lower leg, and the bottom of the foot to the water. Note that the construction of the leg is such that only a relative degree of force can be exerted in a backward direction. Were it possible for humans to extremely hyperextend the knee joint or extend the knee so that the lower part of the leg could move in the forward direction as well as backward, the opportunities for added propulsion would be exceptional. One could perform a perfect undulating movement that would permit a constant application of force backward such as is possible for such marine animals as the porpoise or whale or dolphin. In any case, the human attempts to simulate the undulating movement to the greatest degree possible.

The downbeat of the leg continues with the fully extended knee and ankle until the heel reaches a depth of about 18 in.; the leg is then ready to commence the upbeat.

The upbeat of the leg

When the leg reaches the lowest point on the downbeat, it is ready to start up and the leg bends perceptibly at the knee, while the foot remains extended.

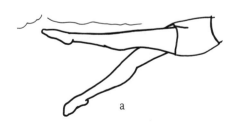
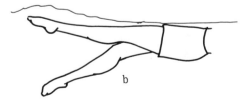
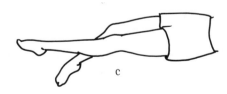

Figure 8.5(a)-(c) Leg action sequence

The leg movement at this point becomes a true kick (in the sense of kicking a ball). The force of the water against the instep and lower leg will assist in achieving the flexed or bent position of the knee and extension of the ankle. The objective is to engage the water with the instep of the foot and the upper surface of the lower leg and to exert force backward as the leg is raised (see Figures 8.5 a, b, and c). When the leg is at its highest point on the upbeat, straighten it to begin the downbeat. Bending the knees excessively on the downbeat will catch water on the back of the lower leg, thus exerting force in the opposite direction from that desired; kicking too deeply will cause an excessive drag below the body and retard forward progress.

The timing of the legs in kicking

As one leg reaches the height of its lifting or upbeat position, the other leg is at its lowest position on the downbeat action. One may practice the kick as described while assuming the

Figure 8.6 Hands position during leg kicking practice

proper back crawl body position, hands by the side or with the arms fully extended behind the head, on or just below the water surface, with thumbs interlocked (see Figure 8.6).

TOTAL COORDINATION OF THE BACK CRAWL STROKE (EFFICIENCY)

There are two views on the subject of coordinating the arm and leg action. The first, supported by many of the most efficient swimmers and their coaches, is to synchronize a six-beat kick with one complete armstroke. As one leg reaches its highest point on the upbeat, the hand on the opposite side enters the water behind and just outside the shoulder. The legs, executing three kicks during one arm stroke, will be in the alternating position at the start of the second three kicks. On the fourth kick, at the height of the upbeat, the opposite leg is raised as the other hand enters the water. Thus, as one hand is entering the water, the leg on the opposite side is reaching the height of its upbeat. It is helpful to count 1, 2, 3 with each arm stroke.

The second view, more appropriate for senior swimmers, is to emphasize the timing of the arms, subordinating the kick to a role of maintaining good body position. This means that the legs may function independently of the arm action to facilitate the action of the total stroke without a conscious effort for precise synchronization. The incorporation of breathing and its timing in the total stroke have been presented under the section on Preliminary Considerations.

ADAPTATIONS FOR SENIORS

Body position

There is little or no alternative to the correct position in which the body lies nearly parallel to the water surface, even with regard for body roll, which accompanies arm stroking. It is important to concentrate on kicking to maintain good body position. At the least, the contribution of the legs should be to keep the lower part of the body nearly parallel to the water surface. This does not imply that the legs should not contribute to propulsion; however, the senior should give priority to good body position.

Back crawl kick

Conventional kick

The kick for the back crawl should serve to maintain good body position. If the body lies high in the water, the kick may simply contribute to that position without regard for strong propulsive action. Adaptations to the conventional (flutter) kick may be as follows:

The absence of needed flexibility may cause the knees to moderately bend on the downbeat phase of the kick (refer to Stroke Mechanics). The swimmer might easily straighten the legs on the up phase of the kick (see Figures 8.5 a, b, and c). Excessive bending of the knees may impede progress, but some of the negative contributions of the bent leg may be offset by the upward thrust of the lower leg on the upbeat. It is helpful on the upward thrust to extend the ankles to catch as much water as possible on the instep.

Other types of kicks

Some senior swimmers may have difficulty with the conventional leg kick. Other types of kicks, while not conventional (flutter kick) for the back crawl, are appropriate. Some of these are as follows:

1. *Elementary backstroke kick.* Both the whip kick and the V-shaped kick (refer to chapter 5 on Elementary Backstroke, Stroke and Techniques and Progressions) are appropriate should the swimmer prefer either of them or an adaptation. The swimmer may, through experimentation, discover a hybrid derived from the whip kick or the V-shaped kick (see Figure 8.7). The basic principle governing kicks is that they contribute to good body position and forward propulsion. The kick may, therefore, allow an action of a widespread recovery and an exertion of force or pressure in a backward direction.

2. *Sidestroke kick* (scissors kick). A single-action scissors kick may be preferred. (Refer to chapter 6 on Sidestroke). The kick is executed in a diagonal plane by a slight turning of the hips rather than in a horizontal plane as in the ele-

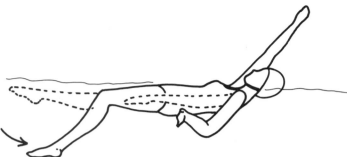

Figure 8.7 Adapted hybrid type kick

mentary backstroke kick. The same principles apply to body position and propulsion. Do not use the legs as in pedaling a bicycle or as in running up a flight of steps.

Back crawl arm stroke

Two types of adaptations can be made in the conventional arm stroke. These are the straight arm stroke and the double arm stroke.

The straight arm stroke

While the bent arm stroke is the most efficient (refer to back crawl stroke techniques and arm stroke), senior swimmers who are inexperienced with it may encounter some difficulties: Concentration on the catch position (as the hand enters the water behind the shoulder), bending the elbow at the appropriate time, and the follow-through motion at the end of the stroke may interfere with total coordination, and pain or injury may result in the shoulder joint of the bent arm at the point where major propulsive emphasis is applied. This is particularly so when the movement is repeated many times or when using a hand paddle to provide resistance so as to build more arm strength. Both problems may be eliminated by using a straight arm during the propulsive phase of the stroke (see Figures 8.8 a and b). While not as efficient as the bent arm, most senior swimmers may prefer the straight-arm style. The propulsive movements of the arm stroke may differ from the bent arm stroke in that the directional path is a fairly straight line and is at a depth of 8 to 10 in. The arm is straight from the time of entry behind and slightly outside the shoulder to the completion of the propulsive phase of the stroke.

There is some flexibility in the placement of the hand as it enters the water. The hand may enter the water behind the head, behind the shoulder, or just outside the shoulder. Select a position for hand placement that is comfortable with no stress or strain. Drop the hand about 6 in. deep and begin the straight arm stroke.

The same general suggestion may be made for the position of the hand on

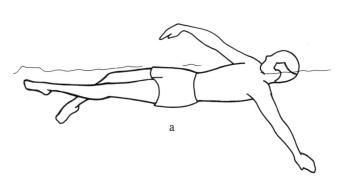

Figure 8.8(a)(b) Straight arm stroke

entering the water as for the hand placement position. Complying with the correct mechanics of the stroke is less important than comfort and effectiveness for the individual in the initial stages of learning. The swimmer may prefer to drop the hand into the water outside the shoulder line in a palm-up position rather than with the palm facing outward. Once the hand enters the water, the swimmer may turn the palm forward (facing toward the feet) and start the propulsive phase of the arm stroke.

Double arm stroke

While the double arm stroke may not strictly qualify as a "crawl" stroke, it nevertheless has been frequently used in backstroke competition among senior swimmers and others. There is some evidence in the literature (Sinclair & Henry, 1916) to indicate that the first person to swim the English Channel unaided by any devices (Captain Webb) alternated a conventional breaststroke with a double overarm backstroke (a variation of the inverted breaststroke). A description of this arm stroke follows:

Starting with both arms at the sides, the arms are simultaneously raised upward and swung backward into the hand placement position described in the conventional position described in the conventional arm stroke (refer to back crawl stroke, and arm and head placement). The backs of the hands may lie on the water surface for comfort and ease (see Figure 8.9 a). The emphasis at first is on reaching and stretching backward (an excellent exercise for flexibility development).

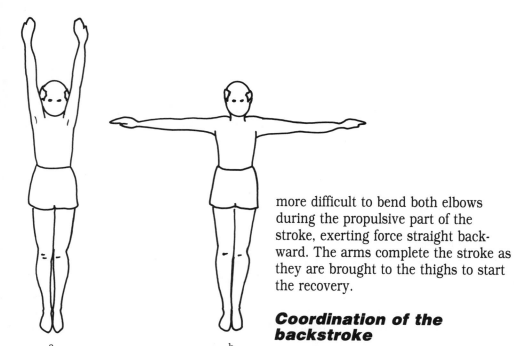

a   b

Figure 8.9(a)(b)   Double arm stroke action

With both arms fully extended, the swimmer pulls and pushes sideward and backward toward the feet (see Figure 8.9 b). It is more efficient but also more difficult to bend both elbows during the propulsive part of the stroke, exerting force straight backward. The arms complete the stroke as they are brought to the thighs to start the recovery.

Coordination of the backstroke

Conventional backstroke

As one arm is entering the water behind and slightly outside the shoulder, the other arm completes the propulsive phase of the stroke and returns to the side. This type of relationship should be maintained.

There may be complete independence between the arms and legs when using the conventional flutter kick. If a choice is made to use a kick other than the flutter kick, experiment with some degree of timing. It can be convenient and helpful to design an individually coordinated stroke. Refer to the following Double Arm Backstroke section.

While breathing is performed independently of the total stroke, remember to inhale through the mouth and exhale through the nose and mouth, principally through the nose. Water is less apt to enter the nose on the recovery phase of the arm stroke when air is being exhaled.

Double-arm backstroke

Various kicks may be used with the double-arm backstroke. These are (a) the conventional back crawl kick (flutter kick), (b) the elementary backstroke kicks (whip kick and V-shaped kick), (c) the scissors kick, and (d) an adaptation of (b) and (c). In most instances, the combinations of kicks with the double-arm backstroke include (b), (c), or (d). A coordinated backstroke with such kicking combinations would be as follows:

1. The basic starting and finishing position of the stroke is one in which the body is fully extended, legs straight, arms by the sides.
2. As the legs begin their recovery (drawn upward), the arms also begin their recovery over the water surface to a position behind and slightly outside the shoulders (see Figure 8.10 a).
3. As the legs begin their propulsive kick, the arms also start their pull-and-push movement.
4. The legs will complete their movement before the arms return to the sides of the body because of the longer range through which the arms must move during the stroke.

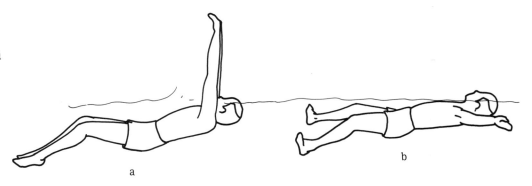

Figure 8.10(a)(b) Total coordinated double arm stroke

This type of coordination provides an excellent example of the law of inertia. The legs initiate movement to overcome inertia followed immediately by a strong propulsive arm stroke. The result is an efficient stroke in terms of total movement over a longer distance and with increased speed (see Figure 8.10 b).

5. The completion of the stroke is marked by a full return of the arms and legs to the starting position. One stroke should be completed fully before another is started.

Conventional armstroke with an adapted leg kick

Many seniors enjoy and are comfortable with the elementary backstroke kick (V-shaped or whip kick) or the sidestroke kick while lying on the back. The coordination in using one of these kicks with the conventional backstroke armstroke (alternate arm action in an over-water recovery) is as follows:

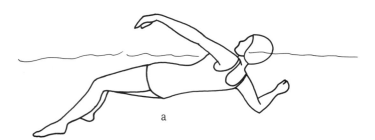

a

1. As the *left* arm, which is extended along the thigh, is raised directly overhead on the recovery and extended back and behind the shoulder, the legs begin their recovery movement (see Figure 8.11 a).

2. Immediately upon completion of the recovery, the legs begin their propulsive action, accompanied by a pulling action of the *left* arm (see Figure 8.11 a-c).

3. As the *right* arm recovers over the water, the legs simultaneously recover (as in Step 1).

b

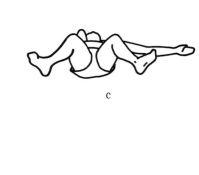

c

Figure 8.11(a)-(c) Conventional arm stroke with adapted kick

4. The legs, again, following recovery begin their propulsive action to be accompanied by the pulling action of the *right* arm.

Note: It will be helpful to remember that as each arm recovers over the water surface, the legs simultaneously recover; with each propulsive action of the legs, one or the other arm is pulling through the stroke.

9 THE FRONT CRAWL STROKE

The front crawl (sometimes termed freestyle) occupies a unique position in the repertoire of swimming strokes among the general population. The alternating arm and leg movements are natural and, because the stroke is recorded to be the fastest and most frequently used of all swim strokes, it has wide social appeal. The senior swimmer, as with all strokes, makes his or her decision on stroke selection in accordance with personal adaptability, limitations, and interests.

PRELIMINARY CONSIDERATIONS

Body position

The body is prone, legs fully extended behind the body, arms fully extended and covering the ears. The face is in the water so that the head maintains a normal position relative to the rest of the body (see Figures 9.1 a and b). Do not lift the head or drop it downward beyond the normal position. The back should be straight, not arched. The eyes should be open at all times and directed forward and downward. Excessive lifting of the head causes the lower body and legs to drop too low, which offers resistance to forward progress and diverts arm action for support rather than for propulsion. The body need not remain flat in the water, a position that interferes with the maximum application of force at variable body positions during stroking; rolling

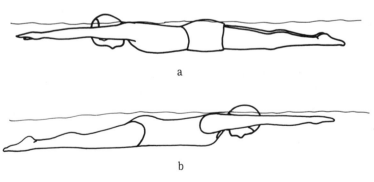

a

b

Figure 9.1(a)(b) Correct body and head position

of the body about 45° to each side on a longitudinal axis during regular stroking movements is natural and helps to maintain good lateral alignment.

Breathing

Special considerations need to be directed toward breathing in the front crawl stroke for the senior swimmer. The swimmer needs to secure maximum ventilation under conditions where full exhalation takes place underwater against resistance, and there is little time available for full inhalation. It is common among senior swimmers to retain air in the lungs during exhalation; the result is that with each succeeding inhalation, less air is inhaled. Providing sufficient oxygen to the cells is a prerequisite to continued activity, but the senior swimmer has less capacity to utilize oxygen than does the younger swimmer.

The senior's aerobic performance is adversely affected by a less resilient thorax or chest cage, less heart strength and contractility, increased resistance to blood flow, less cardiac output, and decreased inspiratory volume with reduced maximum air movement during exercise. While the lungs function normally at rest and during mild exercise, their functioning under stress is limited in the average older person, resulting in decreased oxygenation. Breathing must, therefore, be more rapid for seniors at the same workload because of the decreased vital capacity, yet rapid breathing results in greater resistance to air movement and fatigue to the respiratory muscles (Smith, 1984).

The front crawl breathing technique can provide important benefits when properly executed. Studies have revealed that although there is no chronic effect on lung volume, the swimmer may improve maximum ventilation during exercise, increase blood volume and cardiac output, decrease arterial blood pressure, and increase maximum oxygen consumption (Wiswell, 1980). The front crawl breathing technique when performed as described is therefore an excellent exercise for the senior swimmer.

Eyes open

The eyes should remain open at all times while swimming the front crawl. Keeping the eyes open (a) permits the swimmer to avoid colliding with others, (b) provides a sense of direction and attention to stroke technique, (c) increases sensitivity to the total aquatic environment, and (d) increases the degree of learning progress. Keeping the eyes closed encourages just the opposite results.

Wearing swim goggles will be helpful in preventing eye irritation from chlorine in the pool or salt in ocean water. Swim goggles should be carefully selected according to style and fitting before purchasing. Advice from an experienced swimmer may be helpful.

Flotation devices

The use of a flotation device while practicing the arm stroke or the kick alone (or while swimming the whole stroke) has been suggested and described in the sections of the text that deal with other basic swim strokes. A buoy can be held between the legs to immobilize them while providing support and maintaining good body position. A kickboard held in the hands with arms fully extended is helpful while practicing the front crawl kick (see Figure 9.2). Seniors in Classifications I and II should consider using a flotation device strapped to the waist while practicing the whole stroke (see Figure 9.3).

Out-of-water flexibility exercises

Flexibility in the ankle, knee, and shoulder joints is directly related to the positioning of the legs and arms in the water to secure maximum propulsive power. A description of these positions will be presented in the section on leg kicking and arm stroking. Reference to specific exercise (Figures 11.4 a and b; 11.8; and 11.10 a) may be made by reviewing chapter 11.

Holding pool wall for kicking practice

Prior to practicing the front crawl kick in open water with or without a kick-ing board, it is helpful to review the following leg movements while holding the pool wall: Facing the pool wall, stand in shallow water and grasp with one hand the edge of the pool trough (gutter). Place the palm of the other hand directly below the top hand at a depth of about 18 to 20 in. with the fingers pointing downward toward the floor of the pool (see Figure 7.2). Extend the legs backward. Hold firmly to the wall with the top hand and push against it with the bottom hand; raise the fully extended legs to the water surface and practice the front crawl kick.

Rest whenever the holding position strains the arms. Longer periods of practice will become possible with

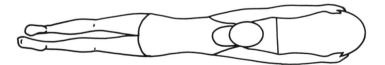

Figure 9.2 Kickboard use for flutter kick practice

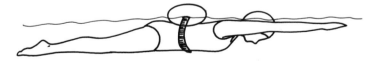

Figure 9.3 Flotation device—stroke practice

repetition of the kicking drill. As the kick becomes more efficient, the wall-holding position will ease.

Terminology in stroke descriptions

A review of texts that present instruction in swimming techniques reveals a variety of terminology. The application of the principles and techniques of swimming within a kinesiological context are admirably expressed by Silvia (1970), Counsilman (1968), and Maglischo (1982), based upon well-established laws of motion and research of recent years. For further information related to the scientific application of the laws of propulsion, refer to the list at the conclusion of this text. Terminology will vary among the references. The presentation for seniors is made in the context of practical understanding and application of a universal nature for the noncompetitive swimmer.

FRONT CRAWL STROKE TECHNIQUES

Body position

The swimmer lies prone in the water with the back straight, not arched. The head is in a normal position, not lifted or dropped. The eyes are directed forward and downward. During stroking, the body will rotate on a longitudinal axis to facilitate arm recovery, to improve breathing position, and to position the arms for more efficient application of force. Additional information on body position for the front crawl is presented under Preliminary Considerations (see Figures 9.1 a and b).

Breathing

Senior swimmers will find it advantageous to breathe on one side only on each complete revolution of the arms rather than holding the breath for a series of arm strokes or breathing on alternate strokes. The reasons for breathing on each complete stroke are related to the increased need for oxygen under conditions of decreased physiological functions that occur with age (see Preliminary Considerations, Breathing section in this chapter). Because there is a tendency to hold part of the inhaled air rather than to exhale completely, the emphasis on breathing on the front crawl will be on exhalation through both nose and mouth, but particularly through the nose. The senior must concentrate on *exhaling fully* while the head is underwater during stroking until the head turns to the side and breaks the water surface to secure another breath. At no time should the swimmer consciously or unconsciously hold any part of the air in the lungs. (For a description of the coordination of breathing with the arm stroke, refer to Arm Stroke and Breathing section later in this chapter.)

Should the swimmer experience difficulty with the exhalation phase of breathing, he or she may practice bobbing as follows:

1. Stand facing the pool wall in the shallow end and grasp the edge of the pool trough (gutter) with both hands.
2. With the trunk in a vertical position, bend the knees to a squatting position. The head will submerge but must be kept in a normal position.
3. Begin to exhale immediately as the head begins to submerge.
4. Continue to exhale through both nose and mouth (while a steady stream of air is exhaled through the nose, water will not enter).
5. Exhale while submerging, while the body reaches its desired depth and as the head returns to the surface. The full exhalation must be timed so that as the head breaks the surface, the swimmer, without hesitation, immediately

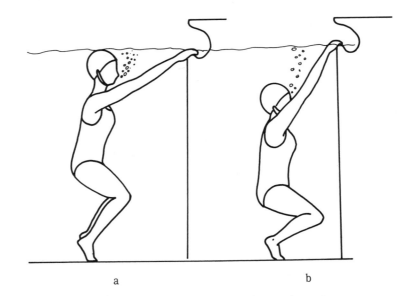

Figure 9.4(a)(b) Bobbing—breath control exercise

starts to inhale (see Figures 9.4 a and b).

The entire exercise is performed slowly and in rhythm with full attention and effort being given to complete exhalation. This exercise should be practiced often—perhaps before stroking practice, during total stroke practice, and upon completion of a swimming period. As the technique is mastered, the swimmer will find a more perfect adaptation and adjustment to crawl stroke breathing.

Crawl arm stroke mechanics

The crawl stroke is an alternating action in which one arm recovers over the water surface to be placed into the water in front of the body while the other arm is exerting force backward through the water under the body in a propulsive action. Simply stated, as one arm is recovering over the water surface, the other is propelling the body forward. Instructions for the crawl arm stroke are given in five phases: hand placement (entry) and extension, catch and adduction with elbow flexion, stroke path to completion, recovery, and timing of both arms.

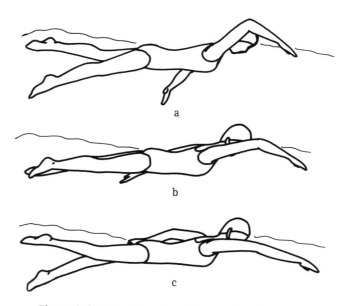

Figure 9.5(a)-(c) Entry—hand placement and extension

Hand placement (entry) and extension

In the first phase, place the hand in the water at a point about half-way between the forehead and the fully extended position. Do not overreach (extending the arm over the water surface), causing the elbow to enter first, or place the hand in the water too close to the forehead. Place the hand deliberately; do not thrust, force, or splash it into the water. Keep the elbow higher than the hand (see Figure 9.5 a), so the fingers enter the water first. With practice the swimmer can consciously feel the fingers enter the water. As the fingers enter the water, extend the arm fully in a forward and downward direction to about 12 to 16 in. deep (see Figures 9.5 b and c).

The catch and adduction with elbow flexion

As the arm completes its fully extended position, it begins to press downward and backward. In this phase, bend the elbow to about a 90° angle to exert force with the palm and the inside surfaces of the lower and upper arm. To prevent the elbow from leading the hand during the adduction (pressing backward), rotate the shoulder inward to assist raising the elbow into the correct position (see Figures 9.6 a, b, and c).

Stroke path to completion

The hand and arm may have a tendency to move a bit outside of the direct backward path. Keep the elbow in its bent position. The palm should face backward, and the entire arm positions for an exertion in a backward path to the thigh (see Figures 9.7 a and b).

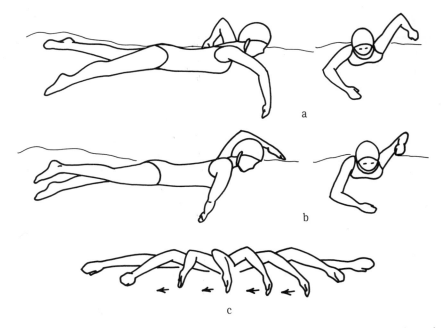

Figure 9.6(a)-(c)   Stroke path to completion: (a-b) elbow bend to 90°; (c) armstroke path

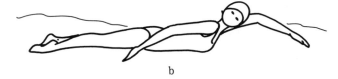

Figure 9.7(a)(b)   Completion of arm stroke by side

The direction of the hand and arm is backward, somewhat outward, and upward to the thigh. Do not permit the hand (palm) to rotate inward during the last one third of the stroke as this causes loss of backward propulsive force. Relax the arm as it reaches the thigh, turn the palm inward a bit, and begin the recovery phase. Always apply the general principle of exerting force backward efficiently, but some variation in the direct path of the stroke is permitted. The stroke should be natural and not forced, and it should conform to sound mechanical principle. For a more complete presentation of the stroke path, consult the texts by Silvia (1970), Counsilman (1968), and Maglischo (1982) listed in the bibliography.

Recovery of the arms

Two types of arm recovery movements should be considered. The first is the high-elbow recovery; the second is the raised hand recovery, which is often

Figure 9.8 Raised elbow on arm recovery

favored by the senior swimmer. (Refer to the Adaptations sections.)

During the high-elbow recovery, when the hand reaches the thigh at the completion of the backward path, raise the arm out of the water with the elbow at a higher position than the hand (see Figure 9.8). Rolling the body to the opposite side assists the arm and hand being raised. Bring the arm forward with the elbow raised high enough to prevent the hand from dragging through the water. As the arm reaches shoulder level, swing the hand forward for entry. Keep the hand relaxed during the recovery action; do not extend it too far away from the body.

A lack of flexibility in the shoulder joint often determines the senior swimmer's preference for the raised-hand

recovery. During the raised-hand recovery, as the hand reaches the thigh at the completion of the backward path, raise the entire arm, with the elbow slightly bent and raised above the water surface. Roll the body to the opposite side to assist the arm and hand being raised. Lift the hand above the elbow, and swing it upward, somewhat outward, and forward (see Figures 9.9 a-d). As the arm reaches shoulder level, bend the elbow and bring the hand downward for entry. The hand-raised recovery seems to facilitate the breathing movement. Whatever style of arm recovery you prefer, two points are important:

1. Do not hesitate or stop as the arm completes its propulsive move-

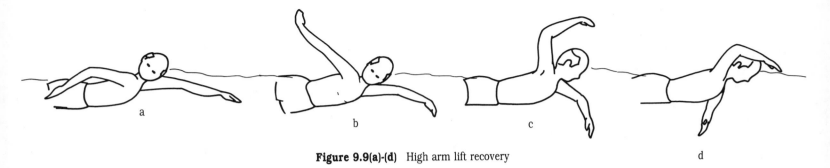

Figure 9.9(a)-(d) High arm lift recovery

ment beside the thigh. Rather, immediately begin recovery action with the hand in an upward and outward sweep to maintain momentum.

2. A body-roll during the arm recovery phase supports and enhances the recovery movement and breathing.

Timing of the arms

The senior swimmer, while keeping in mind both techniques here, should experiment to discover which is more comfortable. Much controversy exists over the specificity of timing. The view here is a fundamental one.

In Timing Style 1, as one arm enters the water during hand placement, the other arm is completing the stroke path beside the thigh; thus, the arms are maintained in the same relative position throughout the entire stroke. That is, as one arm is stroking propulsively, the other is recovering over the water surface (see Figures 9.10 a and b).

Figure 9.10 Timing 1—arms equidistant on stroke

This style is easy to execute and so allows the swimmer to direct attention to other aspects of the total stroke. However, this style is not as mechanically efficient as Timing Style 2 inasmuch as there is an interval when propulsive force is not being applied.

In Timing Style 2, as one arm enters the water for hand placement, the other arm is beneath the body in the middle of its propulsive action (see Figures 9.11 a, b, and c). The application of force is more continuous and the movement is therefore more efficient. Adjustments to the timing techniques should be based upon total stroke, comfort, and ease.

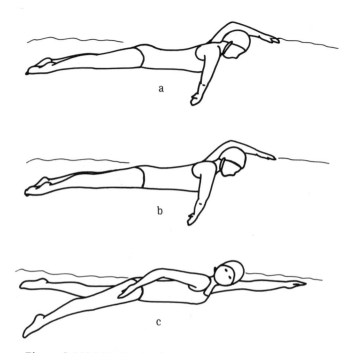

Figure 9.11(a)-(c)   Timing 2—arms overlapping on stroke

Arm stroke and breathing

Breathing during the front crawl is synchronized with the action of the arms and rolling of the body. As the forward arm completes placement fully extended, and the other is in propulsive action under the body (Figures 9.11 a-c), the body rolls to the side and the head turns (not lifts), so the face is out of the water toward the propulsive arm, allowing the swimmer to inhale. In Timing Style 1, the head turns as each arm completes the propulsive action. Exhale immediately on completion of inhalation, as the arm on the breathing side of the body begins recovery while the other arm is in its initial stage of propulsion. To avoid holding a portion of the inhaled air, emphasize complete exhalation.

The flutter kick

The flutter kick is an undulating, alternating leg action in a vertical plane, to a depth of 12 to 16 in. The large muscles of the hips and thighs provide the primary source of power. Initial practice may best be secured by holding on the pool wall as described in Preliminary Considerations.

Phase 1 (upbeat)

When the leg reaches its lowest point on the downbeat, it should be straight, with the ankle extended (see Figure 9.12 a). Raise the straight leg to just beneath the surface with emphasis on exerting force in a backward direction by exposing the surface area of the sole of the foot (plantar flexion) and the back of the lower leg and thigh. To some extent, this inept mechanical action demonstrates one of the disadvantages that the human body possesses

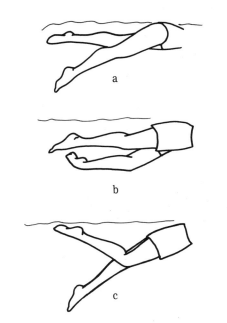

Figure 9.12(a)-(c)   Flutter kick sequence

in seeking propulsion in the water as compared to water mammals.

Phase 2 (downbeat)

Bend the knee moderately as the leg starts downward (see Figures 9.12 b

and c). The knee bend makes possible (a) applying force in a backward direction by exposing the surface of the instep and the front surface of the lower leg, and (b) facilitating the undulating action of the total leg. When the leg reaches its lowest point, straighten it to begin the lifting action.

The swimmer should remember to extend the ankle fully and to bend the knee moderately on the downbeat, straightening the knee on the upbeat. The downbeat phase resembles a whipping action, which is seen at the joint when the leg reaches its lowest point and straightens to begin the lifting action. The emphasis in learning should be on the lifting action in the fully extended position.

The common faults are (a) excessively bending the knees on the upbeat, (b) failing to extend the ankle, (c) kicking too shallowly or too deeply, and (d) keeping the legs too stiff or tight.

After some kick practice holding the wall, the swimmer can use a kickboard to practice (see Figure 9.2).

Timing of the arms and legs

There are two views in timing the arms and legs in the front crawl stroke for the senior swimmer. One view permits leg action independent of the arm stroke. In this view, while the legs may contribute to forward propulsion, their primary purpose is to support the body to maintain good position. In this view the arm stroke is the primary source of propulsion.

The second view supports a six-, four-, or two-beat kick to be synchronized with the arm action. The six-beat kick, most commonly used, executes three down- or upbeats during each single arm stroke. More simply, as in the explanation provided for the synchronization of arms and legs in the back crawl stroke—as the hand and arm are making their placement and entry, the leg on the opposite side is at the height of its upbeat (see Figure 9.10 a). In logical sequence, following three leg kicks (while continuously stroking) when the other hand and arm

are making their placement and entry, the leg on the opposite side is at the height of its upbeat (see Figure 9.5 a). One may view the synchronization for the two-beat kick in the same fashion with, of course, provision for a slowing down or dragging effect of the legs intermittently during the arm stroke.

TOTAL COORDINATION OF THE FRONT CRAWL

An explanation of the total coordinated stroke is provided, to a large extent, in the sections on timing of the arms and legs (p. 102) and on the arm stroke and breathing (p. 100). The senior swimmer may prefer independent action of arms and legs or the use of a two-beat kick (two kicks for each arm stroke). He or she may then better concentrate upon the coordination of the arm stroke and breathing.

Efficiency in swimming the front crawl is determined by counting the number of single arm strokes required to swim a specified distance, compared with the swimmer's prior record or that of a partner with like ability. Some very efficient 70-year-old swimmers have been observed swimming the 25-yard pool length with 14 arm strokes (the number of times each arm recovers over the water surface).

ADAPTATIONS FOR SENIORS

Front crawl breathing technique and arm stroke can be changed only minimally while still maintaining good body position and general efficiency in stroking. If the head is raised to breathe or held above the water while swimming, the body position is disturbed and the arm strokes become largely supporting rather than propulsive movements; the strokes are shortened and only partially completed. Such a style is inefficient and energy demanding; a swimmer would probably not swim far without tiring.

Some modifications on kicking to

accompany front crawl arm stroking are suggested. The senior swimmer should experiment with these.

1. *Minimum kicking.* It is almost impossible not to move the legs in some direction while swimming. Minimum kicking permits the lower part of the body (from the hips to the toes) to remain parallel with the water surface. Any movement that causes the lower body to sink should definitely be discouraged. One may, therefore, consider pulling or dragging both legs behind him or her with only minimum effort in applying a modified type of flutter kick (refer to section on Flutter Kick). Minimum kicking is best effected by the swimmer who has mastered good front crawl breathing technique and who can keep the head down so as to maintain a high-leg position. Keeping the head high will cause the lower body to submerge at too low a depth and destroy good body position.

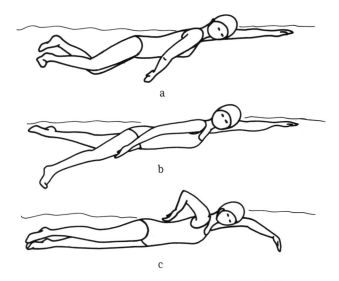

Figure 9.13(a)-(c) Kick adaptation—scissors kick

2. *Sidestroke kicking* (scissors kick). Those who find the sidestroke pleasant and comfortable can incorporate the scissors kick into the front crawl stroke. (Such a stroke, commonly referred to in swimming literature as the Trudgeon Crawl, once occupied a prominent position in the evolution of swim strokes.) A single scissors kick (chapter 6) is executed as the head turns to the side for a breath and as the arm on the breathing side nears completion of its backward movement toward the hip. As the head rotates back into the water after inhalation, the kick is completed and the legs are held together for the glide (see Figures 9.13 a, b, and c).

3. *Hybrid kicking*. Other styles of kicking may be natural and comfortable to the senior. Any kick used should support the lower body parallel to the surface of the water. Seniors who prefer a natural breaststroke kick of the conventional type often find it comfortable to use a modified version of this kick (see Figures 9.14 a-d). Swimmers need to experiment with the suggested styles.

Figure 9.14(a)-(d)   Kick adaptation—breaststroke kick

10 IN-WATER EXERCISES

Both in-water and out-of-water exercises are intended primarily to improve strength, muscular endurance, and joint flexibility for swimming, but they may be useful for other purposes as well. Physicians and physical therapists often recommend postoperative rehabilitative in-water exercises. The in-water exercises for swimmers may be useful for this purpose.

In recent years, there has been an increased interest in exercises performed in the water by physically capable younger persons, athletes, and the elderly. Water, probably the oldest medium of physical treatment, may also be the most effective for rehabilitation (Lowman, Roen, Aust, & Paull, 1937) because exercises are easier to perform in water than against normal gravitational pressure.

SOME FACTS ABOUT EXERCISING IN WATER

1. Warm water is helpful when performing exercises to restore muscular strength or to improve the range of motion of a joint. Modern pools usually maintain a range of water temperatures conducive to water exercises. Warm water dilates the peripheral blood vessels, improving the interchange of fluids within the part exercised. While the use of ice in peripheral massage is readily recognized, our concern here is with the swimming pool environment.

2. The pressure of water upon an immersed part of the body (abdomen, chest) may cause sufficient resistance to contribute to the development of strength, to increase the speed of circulatory exchange, and to facilitate the return of venous blood (Lowman, Roen, Aust, & Paull, 1937).

3. Muscular tension and spasm are lessened by the sedative effect of warm water on the nervous system. This permits exercising a part over a longer range of motion by relaxing tight muscles, interrupting the vicious cycle of spasm and pain.

4. Absence of the pull of gravity allows greater freedom of movement and, in cases of restoration, less resistance and stress, and increased range of motion.

5. The buoyancy provided by immersion in water may be thought of as an assistive force with the forces of

gravity removed (raising the body part to the surface) or as a resistive force (submerging the body part to overcome buoyancy).

6. The elimination of weight on a body joint or joint friction caused by parts that surround it (e.g., the shoulder) and consequent pain caused when lifting the parts may be lessened, and this makes joint action possible with little or no pain and permits a larger arc of movement.

7. In water the entire body or any of its parts can move in any plane. Observe, for example, the movements of solo synchronized swimmers in practice or competition. Water permits all types of movements, some of which cannot be similarly executed elsewhere. Possible are all types of circumduction movements from either horizontal or vertical axes, in lateral (side to side), longitudinal (forward and back), or vertical (up and down) planes.

8. Any increase in muscular strength is related to the speed of movement of a body part through the water and to the degree of body surface area exposed to the direction of movement. It takes more strength to move the arm through the water when the palm is at a right angle to the water surface than when it is parallel to it.

9. The satisfaction and pleasure of accomplishing a variety of exercises in the water may increase interest in learning to swim better.

GUIDELINES FOR PARTICIPATING

Some helpful guidelines are offered to seniors who wish to engage in the in-water exercise program:

1. Individual swimmers can decide on an exercise program based upon a prior period of exploration and experimentation. No effort is made to prescribe exercises for everyone in view of the evidence provided in chapter 1, which presents the characteristics of seniors.

2. The type of exercise to meet a specific purpose can be determined by the senior or the swimmer may select a balanced and progressive program that includes at least one exercise for each body part.

3. The principles that govern the out-of-water exercises presented in chapter 11 also apply to the in-water exercise program. Review these principles as a sound basis on which to plan and engage in such a program.

4. Always consider the position of the body in relation to the part to be exercised. These positions are listed with the exercises. These are: (a) partner assisting, (b) holding on pool wall, (c) use of a flotation device, and (d) freestanding.

5. Each exercise and its alternate may be varied by extending or bending the lever arm (increasing

or decreasing the degree of strength needed), changing the speed of the movement, changing the position of specific parts of the body, or by using a flotation or resistance device (kick board or hand paddle).

6. The senior should be especially sensitive to becoming chilled while in the water. If this occurs, either swim vigorously for a while or take a warm shower immediately.

7. The duration and intensity of any single exercise period should be determined by the Affective Fatigue Scale (chapter 2) or by a sensitivity to chilling.

IN-WATER EXERCISES

The following exercises should be performed in the shallow end of the pool:

Arms and shoulders

Figures 10.1 a and b—*The arm press*

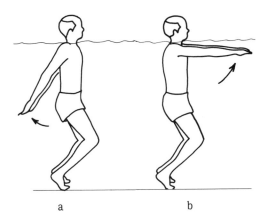

Figure 10.1(a)(b) The arm press

1. Stand in waist deep water.
2. Bend knees, body erect, until water covers shoulders.
3. Arms extended forward underwater at shoulder level parallel to water surface, *palms facing down.*
4. Keep arms straight, press downward and backward as far as possible (Figure 10.1 a).
5. Keep arms straight, raise arms forward and upward to starting position (Figure 10.1 b).
6. Repeat 6 to 10 times.

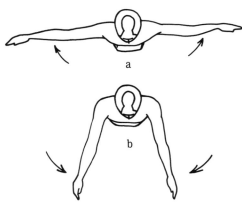

Figure 10.2(a)(b) The arm squeeze

Figures 10.2 a and b—*The arm squeeze*

1. Same body position as in Figure 10.1.
2. Same starting position, but with *palms facing each other.*
3. Keeping arms straight, press sideward and backward as far as possible (Figure 10.2 a).
4. Keeping arms straight, press sideward and forward to starting position (Figure 10.2 b).
5. Repeat 6 to 10 times.

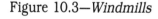

Figure 10.3 Windmills

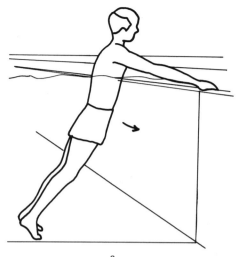

a

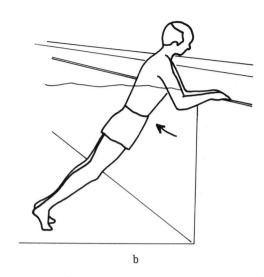

b

Figure 10.4(a)(b) The dipper (wall push)

Figure 10.3—*Windmills*

1. Same body position as in 10.1 a.
2. Extend arms sidewards under water at shoulder level, parallel to water surface, *palms facing forward*.
3. Keeping arms straight, slowly rotate arms at shoulder level so that hands describe a circle of approximately 12 in. in diameter (Figure 10.3).
4. Circle 6 to 12 times.

Figures 10.4 a and b—*The dipper* (wall push)

1. Stand in water, facing pool wall, water at midline of chest, feet 18 to 24 in. from pool wall.
2. Place both hands on pool trough (gutter) so body is straight and in inclined position with arms straight (Figure 10.4 a).
3. Bend both elbows so face is close to pool edge. Keep elbows up (Figure 10.4 b).
4. Extend arms to straight position by pushing away from wall.
5. Repeat 6 to 10 times.

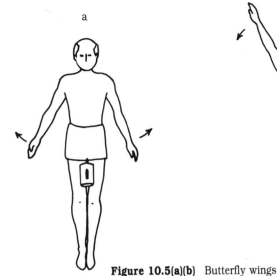

a

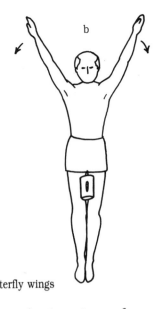

b

Figure 10.5(a)(b) Butterfly wings

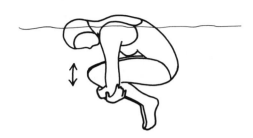

Figure 10.6 Knee hug

Back stretching and strengthening

Figure 10.6—*Knee hug*

Figures 10.5 a and b—*Butterfly wings*

1. Lie on back in shallow water, arms by sides, palms facing thighs at right angles to water surface.
2. Legs may be supported by a partner, feet may be hooked under a ladder step, or a flotation device may be used.
3. With arms straight, palms at right angles to water surface, press sideward and backward to full extension behind head, always keeping arms under water (Figure 10.5 a).
4. With arms straight, palms at right angles to water surface, press arms outward, sideward, and backward toward feet, to starting position (Figure 10.5 b).
5. Repeat 6 to 10 times.

1. Take a full breath and hold it. Place face in water, draw both knees up to chest, grasping legs below knees. Keep head down toward knees.
2. Pull knees to chest in rhythmical movements, stretching muscles of lower back.
3. Repeat as many times as possible while holding the breath.

Figure 10.7 Back stretcher

Figure 10.7—*Back stretcher*

1. In shoulder-deep water, place back against pool wall. Place hands over shoulders, grasping pool trough (gutter edge).
2. Draw both knees upward to water surface.
3. Draw both knees toward chest. In drawn-up position, pull knees to chest in rhythmical movements to stretch muscles of the lower back.

Figure 10.8—*Alternate backward leg lift*

1. In shoulder-deep water, *face* the pool wall with both hands on

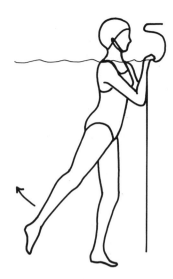

Figure 10.8 Alternate backward leg lift

trough (gutter). Place both elbows against wall directly under hands.
2. With trunk and legs straight, slowly raise *one* leg backward and upward as body structure will permit. Do not twist trunk. Lower leg to starting position. Repeat 6 to 10 times.
3. Repeat exercise with other leg.

Figure 10.9 Back strengthener

Figure 10.10 Abdominal strengthener

Figure 10.9—*Back strengthener*

1. Same position as preceding exercise.
2. With trunk and legs straight, *slowly* raise both legs backward and upward to water surface in a horizontal position.
3. Hold horizontal position for count of 3 seconds.
4. Lower *straight* trunk and legs to pool bottom.
5. Repeat 2 or 3 times, resting between exercises.

NOTE: Practicing a swimming kick such as the front or breaststroke kick while holding the wall will help to strengthen back muscles.

Abdomen

Figure 10.10—*Abdominal strengthener*

1. In shoulder-deep water, stand with back against pool wall. Place both hands over shoulders, grasping pool trough (gutter edge). Keep back of shoulders firmly against pool wall.
2. Draw in abdomen. Keeping trunk and legs straight, slowly raise both legs forward and upward to water surface in horizontal position.
3. Hold horizontal position for count of 3 seconds.
4. Lower straight trunk and legs to pool bottom to starting position.
5. Repeat 2 or 3 times, resting between exercises.

Figure 10.11—*Sit-ups*

1. Lie face up, arms relaxed by sides. Have a partner assist by holding

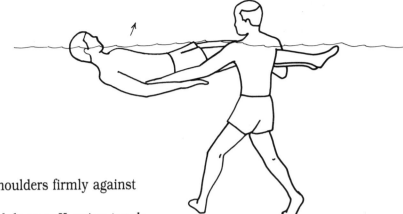

Figure 10.11 Sit-ups

both legs with one arm, and by placing other hand under swimmer's back.

2. Draw in abdomen slightly. Slowly raise head slightly upward, then raise upper trunk to about one-eighth sitting position.
3. Hold for 3 seconds. Lower head and trunk.
4. Repeat 3 or 4 times, resting between exercises.

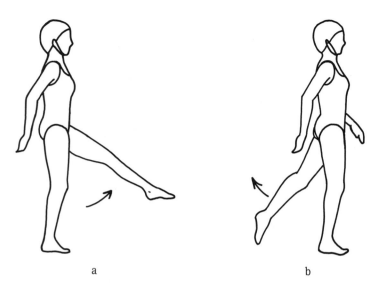

a

b

Figure 10.12(a)(b) The punter

Figure 10.13 Sideward leg lift

Legs and hips

Figures 10.12 a and b—*The punter*

1. Stand in chest-deep water, arms by sides, or use hands for support. Keep legs and trunk straight.

2. Raise one leg forward and upward as high as possible (Figure 10.12 a). Return to starting position. Extend same leg backward (Figure 10.12 b). Keep trunk erect. Repeat 6-10 times.

3. Repeat exercise with opposite leg.

Figure 10.13—*Sideward leg lift*

1. Stand in waist-deep water, one side toward pool wall. Incline body toward pool wall enough to submerge shoulders. Grasp pool edge with bottom hand, elbow against wall, other hand by side. Keep body straight in inclined position.

2. Keep legs straight, raise top leg

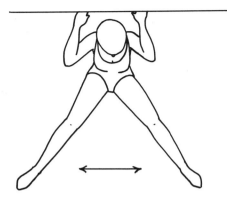

Figure 10.14 The split

upward as high as possible. Hold for 3 seconds. Return to starting position. Repeat 6 to 10 times.
3. Repeat exercise with opposite leg, reversing position.
NOTE: Above exercises may be performed with partner offering resistance by placing hand on leg during lift.

Figure 10.14—*The split*

1. In waist-deep water, place back against pool wall, hands over shoulders, grasping trough edge. Raise both legs straight and together, parallel with water surface. Hold back of shoulders to wall.
2. Keeping legs straight, press each leg sideward and outward as far as possible. Hold for 3 seconds.
3. Return to starting position, keeping legs straight.
4. Repeat 6 to 10 times.

Figures 10.15 a and b—*Knee spread*

1. Hold pool wall on back as described in previous exercise.
2. Draw knees upward toward chin, keeping legs under water surface. Keep back of shoulders in contact with pool wall.
3. Spread knees laterally as far as possible. Keep heels together (a). Hold for 3-second count. Bring knees together to starting position (b).
4. Repeat exercise 6 to 10 times.

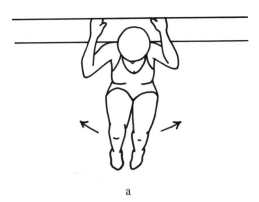

a

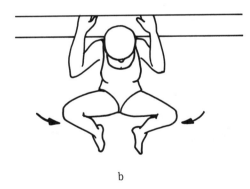

b

Figure 10.15(a)(b) Knee spread

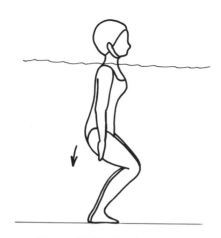

Figure 10.16 Tendon stretcher

Figure 10.16—*Tendon stretcher*

1. In waist-deep water, standing straight, place hands on hips or leave free for balancing.
2. Keep trunk straight. Bend knees to a squat position in water at neck depth.
NOTE: At full squat, keep feet flat on pool bottom to stretch Achilles tendon.

3. Return to full-standing position.
4. Repeat exercise 6 to 10 times.
NOTE: Elementary back and breast-stroke leg kick practices on a wall are excellent hip and leg exercises (see chapters 5 and 7).

Aerobic exercise

The progression through successive classifications in the *Swimming For Seniors* program creates conditions for sufficient aerobic exercise. Seniors who have not yet reached Classification I may consider the following:

1. In water 5 to 6 ft deep, using a flotation device or assisted by a partner, assume a vertical or nearly vertical body position. Use hands for sculling for additional support (refer to chapter 5 on hand sculling). Use one or a variety of leg kicks (e.g., breast, scissors, flutter, bicycle). Refer to chapters of text on basic strokes for description of various kicks. The length of time for aerobic exercising can be determined by the application of the Affective Fatigue Scale.

11 OUT-OF-WATER EXERCISES

Qualities contributing to improved swimming that can be developed through specific exercises or conditioning are muscular strength and endurance, cardiorespiratory endurance, and flexibility. Although the out-of-water exercises selected for presentation to senior swimmers deal primarily with flexibility, some will also increase muscular endurance. For example, exercises to stretch the muscles of the lower back will also involve strengthening the abdominal muscles.

The development of strength for strength's sake is not an objective of the swimming program; rather, it is considered only as it contributes to effective development of stroke skill and swimming performance. The constant repetition of movement against a resistance during swimming at a duration, frequency, and intensity chosen by the individual should produce suffi-cient improvement of muscular and cardiorespiratory endurance in seniors.

The flexibility exercises serve two major purposes. The first purpose is to improve swimming skills. The three criteria by which swimming performance for seniors is judged are (a) body position, (b) specific stroke mechanics, and (c) general efficiency of the total stroke. Increasing the range of movement around joints increases efficiency in general and improves the specific mechanics of the stroke. For example, with increased flexibility of the shoulders, the swimmer is able to fully extend the arms. This, in turn, increases the degree of application of force to move over a greater distance per stroke, increases the resting phase per glide, requires fewer strokes per distance, and secures added anatomical and physiological benefits.

The second purpose of flexibility ex-ercises is related to the improvement of life functions physically and psychologically. Studies reveal that the correct use of the body as an instrument of expression or as a means of enjoying life more fully (as contrasted with conditions of poor mechanical usage or in poor posture) contributes to efficiency of movement in walking, sitting, and standing, to a reduction of mental and muscular fatigue, and to good appearance. Stretching also helps to reduce muscle tension and relaxes the body. As you stretch parts of the body, you become more aware of them, and you become better prepared for your activity. Loss of flexibility with a reduction of normal movement in turn contributes to a continued loss of flexibility. Poor posture in sitting or standing contributes to a continued deterioration through a shortening effect of the muscles. For example, shortening the chest muscles causes the shoulders to project forward and the back to become rounded; this decreases movement in the shoulders and back, leading to further deterioration. Optimum flexibility of the joint surfaces, therefore, adds to ease and efficiency of movement, provides a pleasing aesthetic appearance, and reduces mental and physical fatigue.

GUIDELINES FOR PARTICIPATING

The following considerations preliminary to engaging in flexibility exercises will be helpful in assisting the senior swimmer to achieve optimum results and to relieve concerns or questions related to exercising:

1. The flexibility exercises in the following section are selected specifically with the senior swimmer in mind. Other means of producing greater degrees of flexibility require special equipment, a partner resisting, or paired stretching, which may be difficult for seniors to obtain.

2. The earlier and perhaps most beneficial results from a stretching exercise may be achieved by applying heat to the area to be exercised. Stretching the part may be done after heat has been applied or while heat is being applied. If exercising while under a warm or hot shower, heat the area well; then bend or stretch holding a position of stretch for 4 to 6 seconds, extending the part a bit more each time.

3. It may not be necessary to perform all the exercises indicated, or all the exercises in any single area. The individual senior should determine the choice of exercises according to need and experimentation.

4. The exercises should be performed every day. Their application may be made prior to entry into the water (in shower or on pool deck) or at home (preferably in the morning soon after rising). Ideally the senior should incorporate them into the daily routine of life.

5. The flexibility exercises most related to swimming performance are those associated with the shoulder, knee, ankle, and neck joints. Breathing in all strokes (particularly the front crawl because of the turning of the head) and head support in other strokes require good flexibility.

6. Swimming in itself is a stretching exercise because the application of force is always affected by a preliminary stretching movement of the arms, shoulders, knees, or ankles. Therefore, stretching exercises performed out-of-water supplement and complement swimming.

7. Stretching exercises are useful in the warm-up procedure prior to entering the water. Such exercises may help to prevent muscular in-

juries caused by sudden exertion or stretching.

EXERCISES

The neck

Figures 11.1 a-d—*Neck stretching*

Note: Standing in a shower and permitting warm water to bathe the neck for 2 to 3 minutes will be most helpful before and during these exercises.

1. Tilt the head from one side to the other, 5 times to each side (Figure 11.1 a).
2. Turn or pivot the head, left to right, 5 times to each side (Figure 11.1 b).
3. Bend the head forward then backward, 5 times each movement (Figure 11.1 c).
4. Roll the head in circles, first to the right, then to the left, 2 times each direction (Figure 11.1 d).

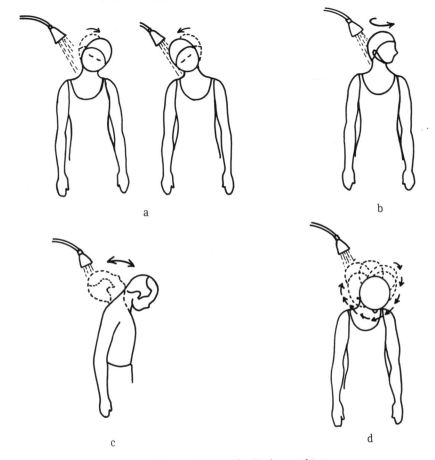

Figure 11.1(a)-(d)   Neck stretching

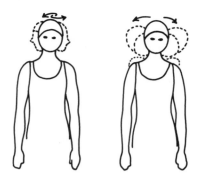

Figure 11.2(a)(b) Neck turn and tilt

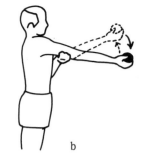

Figure 11.3(a)(b) Elbow (a) extensor (b) depressor

Figures 11.2 a-b—*Neck turn and tilt*

1. Turn the head to the right as far as you can. Hold for 3 seconds, return to normal position and relax for 1 second (see Figure 11.2 a). Repeat 3 times.
2. Repeat on the left side.
3. Tilt the head to the right (ear to shoulder). Hold 3 seconds; return to normal position and relax for 1 second (see Figure 11.2 b). Repeat 3 times.
4. Repeat on the left side.

The elbow

Note: Many exercises for the extension of the elbow are included with those designed for the shoulders.

Figure 11.3 a—*Elbow extensor*

1. Fully extend the right arm forward at shoulder level. Place the left hand under the right arm just above the elbow for support. Bend the right arm at the elbow, moving the hand upward about 5 or 6 inches. Drop the lower arm in a relaxed manner while holding the upper arm at shoulder level with the left hand (see Figure 11.3 a). Repeat 6 times.
2. Repeat with the left arm and elbow.

Figure 11.3 b—*Elbow depressor*

1. Extend right arm and support as shown in Figure 11.3 a, holding a 1-pound weight in the right hand. Fully support the right arm just above the elbow (see Figure 11.3 b). Hold in a relaxed manner for 6 seconds.
2. Repeat exercise with left arm.

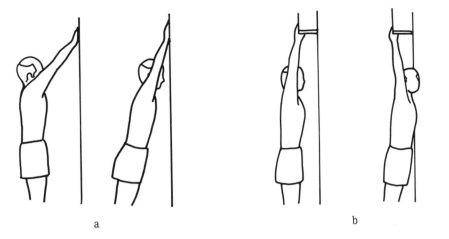

Figure 11.4(a)(b) Overhead shoulder stretcher (a) stretcher (b) extensor

The shoulder

Note: These exercises may serve both purposes of muscle strengthening and joint stretching.

Figure 11.4 a—*Overhead shoulder stretcher*

1. Stand facing the wall at a distance of about 2 feet.

2. Lean forward, extend both arms and place the hands overhead against the wall.

3. With the knees, back, and elbows straight, lean forward until a stretching in the upper chest and shoulders is felt (see Figure 11.4 a). Hold for 6 seconds, relax for 1 second. Repeat 4 times.

4. A greater degree of stretching in each shoulder may be achieved by leaning forward more to one side, then toward the other.

Figure 11.4 b—*Overhead shoulder extensor*

1. Stand directly in the center of a door frame (doorway). Place both hands overhead against the inside edge of the frame. Keep the trunk, knees, and elbows straight.

2. Lean forward as far as possible until a stretching of the upper chest and shoulders is felt (see Figure 11.4 b). Hold for 6 seconds, relax 1 second. Repeat 4 times.

3. A greater degree of stretching on each shoulder may be achieved by leaning more toward one side, then toward the other.

Figure 11.5—*Side/shoulder stretcher*

1. Stand directly in the center of a door frame (doorway). Extend arms to the sides at shoulder level and press against the inside of the

Figure 11.5 Side shoulder stretcher

door frame (see Figure 11.5).
2. With the back, knees, and elbows straight and the abdomen in, lean forward as far as possible until you can feel the upper chest and shoul-

Figure 11.6 Wall push

ders stretching. Hold 6 seconds; relax 1 second. Repeat 4 times.
Note: This exercise may also be used for muscle strengthening. Each time, when the body has reached a full forward position, press with both arms to regain the normal standing position.

Figure 11.6—*Wall push*

1. Stand facing a corner of a room, at arms' length from the corner. Maintain a good body position by keeping the back and knees straight and the abdomen in.
2. Touch one wall with each hand at shoulder level, fingers pointing upward.
3. Lean forward, with the back and knees straight, bending the elbows until the forehead touches or nearly touches the corner. At this point you should be able to feel the chest and shoulders stretching (see Figure 11.6).
4. Hold for a count of 6 seconds; then return to the starting position.
Note: This exercise may also be used for muscle strengthening by pushing hard with both hands to regain the starting position upon completion of the stretch.

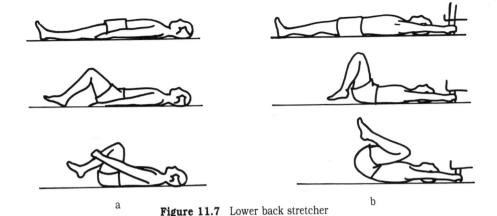

Figure 11.7 Lower back stretcher

a   b

The lower back

Note: The exercises indicated will serve both purposes of stretching the lower back and strengthening the abdominal muscles.

Figure 11.7 a—*Lower back stretcher* (A)

1. Lie on the back, legs together and straight, arms by the sides.

2. Push the lower back toward the floor. Bend knees, drawing them toward the chest.
3. With hands placed below the knees, pull them toward the head.
4. Keep the heels as close to the buttocks as possible. Hold the knees to the chest for 3 seconds.
5. Lower the knees about 12 in. and relax for 1 second but keep hands on the legs.

6. Repeat 6 times slowly.

Figure 11.7 b—*Lower back stretcher* (B)

1. Lie on the back, legs together and straight.
2. Place the hands overhead and grasp a stable object (e.g., the leg of a sofa, bed, or bureau). Keep lower back against the floor by drawing in the abdomen and contracting the abdominal muscles.
3. Bend knees, drawing them toward the chest. Keep the heels close to the buttocks at all times.
4. Draw the knees slowly toward the chin; then lower slowly about 12 in., continuing to hold the object (see Figure 11.7 b). Repeat raising and lowering the knees 6 to 8 times.

Note: Should this exercise seem too strenuous, substitute the exercise shown in Figure 11.7 a.

Figure 11.8 Hamstring stretcher

The knee (hamstring muscles)

Note: The purposes of these exercises are to stretch the long back muscles as the trunk bends downward and to strengthen them as the trunk rises, to increase the flexibility of the hip joints and spine, and to stretch the muscles on the backs of thighs and knees.

Figure 11.8—*Hamstring stretcher*

1. Sit upright on the floor, legs straight a few inches apart. Clasp the hands behind the head, elbows forward, abdomen drawn in.
2. Keeping the knees absolutely straight, bend forward attempting to touch the elbows to the knees (see Figure 11.8).
3. Return to right-angle sitting position as in 1. Repeat 10 to 12 times.

Figure 11.9 Knee pusher

Figure 11.9—*Knee pusher*

1. Stand straight with arms to the sides.
2. Cross the right leg with the left leg with the legs nearly parallel and the feet close together on the floor. Press the left leg backward against the right leg (see Figure 11.9).
3. Bend forward and downward attempting to touch the floor beside the feet. Stretch for 6 seconds and return to upright position. Repeat 3 times.
4. Repeat with other leg.

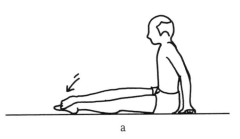

Figure 11.10 Ankle stretcher (a) sitting (b) kneeling

The ankle

Note: Two types of exercises are presented: (a) ankle stretching (plantar flexion) and (b) achilles tendon stretching (dorsi-flexion).

Figure 11.10 a—*Ankle stretcher—sitting*

1. Sit on floor, legs extended and together, hands on floor by sides.
2. Extend the left foot forward as much as possible. Place the sole of the right foot on top of the left ankle and exert force downward so as to stretch the left ankle (see Figure 11.10 a).

3. Hold pressure for 6 seconds; rest 1 second. Repeat 6 times.
4. Repeat exercise on the right ankle.

Figure 11.10 b—*Ankle stretcher—kneeling*

1. Kneel on the floor. Extend both feet backward on a soft towel or pad.
2. Sit back on the soles of the feet. Additional pressure on ankle extension may be made by extending the body backward and rocking backward slightly (see Figure 8.4b).
3. Rock backward slowly 4 times. Rest and repeat 3 times.

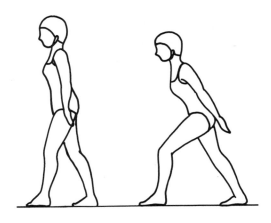

Figure 11.11 Achilles tendon stretcher

Figure 11.11—*Achilles tendon stretcher*

1. Standing, place the left foot about 18 in. in front of the right foot, arms at sides.
2. Lean forward bending the left knee. Keep the right leg straight and the heel on the floor. Tension should be felt in the back of the ankle and knee of the right leg (Figure 11.11).

3. Hold the stretch position for 4 seconds. Rest 1 second. Repeat 4 times.
4. Repeat with the right leg in the forward position.

Figure 11.12—*Ankle flexor*

1. Place an object (books or boards 3 in. high) against the inside of a door frame. Grasping the sides of the door frame, place the soles of the feet on the edge of the books (platform) with the heels on the floor.
2. Keeping the body straight, pull the body forward so that the forehead is close to the frame (see Figure 11.12). Tension should be felt in the backs of the ankles and knees.
3. Hold stretched position for 4 seconds; rest 1 second. Repeat 4 times.

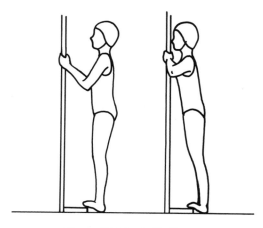

Figure 11.12 Ankle flexor

REFERENCES

American College of Sports Medicine. (1980). *Guidelines for graded testing and exercise prescriptions* (2nd ed.). Philadelphia: Lea & Febiger.

Åstrand, P.O., & Rodahl, K. (1977). *Textbook of work physiology*. New York: McGraw-Hill.

Barry, J.R., & Wingrove, C.R. (1977). *Let's learn about aging*. New York: Wiley.

Birren, J.E. (Ed.). (1959). *Handbook of aging and the individual*. Chicago: University of Chicago Press.

Birren, J.E., Butler, R.N., Greenhouse, S.W., Sokoloff, L., & Yarrow, M.R. (1976). *Human aging: A biological and behavioral study*. Public Health Service Publication (pp. 77-122). Washington, DC: U.S. Department of Health, Education and Welfare.

Bolton, E., & Goodwin, D. (1967). *An introduction to pool exercises*. London: E. and S. Livingstone Ltd.

Borg, G. (1978). Subjective effort in relation to physical performance and working capacity. In H.L. Pick, H.W. Leibowitz, J.E. Singer, A. Steinschneider, & H.W. Stevenson (Eds.), *Psychology from research to practice* (pp. 333-361). New York: Plenum Press.

Bortz, W. (1980). Effect of exercise on aging—Effect of aging on exercise. *Journal of the American Geriatric Society*, **28**, 49-51.

Brunner, D., & Jokl, E. (Eds.). (1970). *Physical activity and aging: Medicine and sport* (Vol. 4). Basel, Switzerland: S. Karger.

Colson, J.H.C. (1969). *Progressive exercise therapy in rehabilitation and physical education*. Bristol: John Wright & Sons.

Costill, D. (1984). The facts are in: Stress those sprint muscles and increase performance. *Swim Swim*, **6**, (Summer), 12-14.

Counsilman, J.E. (1968). *The science of swimming*. Englewood Cliffs, NJ: Prentice-Hall.

Cureton, T.K., Jr. (1965). *Physical fitness and dynamic health*. New York: Dial Press.

deVries, H.A. (1977). Physiology of physical conditioning for the elderly. In R. Harris & L.J. Frankel (Eds.), *Guide to fitness after fifty* (pp. 47-52). New York: Plenum Press.

Duffield, M.H. (Ed.). (1969). *Exercises in the water*. London: Bailliere, Tindall & Cassell.

Eriksson, M.D., & Furberg, B. (1978). *Swimming medicine IV: International series on sport sciences* (Vol. 6). Baltimore: University Park Press.

Finch, C.E., & Hayflick, L. (Eds.). (1977). *Handbook of the biology of aging*. New York: Van Nostrand Reinhold.

Fitts, R.H. (1981). Aging and skeletal muscle. In E.L. Smith & R.C. Serfass (Eds.), *Exercise and aging: The scientific basis* (pp. 31-44). Hillside, NJ: Enslow.

Fletcher, G.F. (1982). *Exercise in the practice of medicine*. Mount Kisco, NY: Futura.

Fries, J.F., & Crapo, L.M. (1981). *Vitality and aging: Implications of the rectangular curve*. San Francisco: Freeman.

Fryer, J.H. (1962). Studies of body composition in men aged 60 and over. In N.W. Shock (Ed.), *Biological aspects of aging* (pp. 73-81). New York: Columbia University Press.

George, L.K., & Beardon, L.B. (1980). *Quality of life in older persons*. New York: Human Sciences Press.

Goldman, R., & Rockstein, M. (Eds.). (1975). *The physiology and pathology of human aging*. New York: Academic Press.

Harris, R., & Frankel, L.J. (Eds.). (1978). *Guide to fitness after fifty*. New York: Plenum Press.

Haynes, S.G., & Feinleib, M. (1980). Women, work and coronary heart disease: Prospective findings from the Framingham heart study. *American Journal of Public Health*, **70**, 133-141.

Heath, G.W., Hagberg, J.M., Ehsani, A.A., & Holloszy, J.O. (1981). A physiological comparison of young and older endurance athletes. *Journal of Applied Physiology*, **51**, 634-640.

Heikkinen, E., & Kayhty, B. (1977). Gerontological aspects of physical activity: Motivation of older people in physical training. In R. Harris & L.J. Frankel (Eds.), *Guide to fitness after fifty* (pp. 191-205). New York: Plenum Press.

Hickey, T. (1980). *Health and aging*. Monterey, CA: Brooks/Cole.

Hollis, M. (1976). *Practical exercise therapy*. London: Blackwell.

Holloszy, J.O. (1983). Exercise, health, and aging: A need for more information. *Medicine and Science in Sports and Exercise*, **15**, 1-5.

Holmer, I. (1974). Physiology of swimming man. *Acta Physiologica Scandinavica*, **90**, (Suppl. 407), 9-55.

Holt, L.E. (1974). *Scientific stretching for sport*. Halifax, Nova Scotia: Dalhousie University.

Johnston, P.W. (Ed.). (1981). *Perspectives on aging*. Cambridge, MA: Ballinger.

Kasch, F.W. (1976). The effects of exercise on the aging process. *The Physician and Sports Medicine*, **4**, 64-68.

Kendall, H.O., Kendall, F.P., & Wadsworth, G.E. (1971). *Muscles: Testing and function*. Baltimore: Williams & Wilkins.

Komi, P.V. (Ed.). (1979). *Exercise and sport biology: International series on sport sciences* (Vol 12). Champaign, IL: Human Kinetics.

Lowenthal, D. (Ed.). (1979). *Therapy through exercise*. London: Grune & Stratton.

Lowman, C.L., Roen, S.G., Aust, R., & Paull, H. (1937). *Technique of underwater gymnastics*. Los Angeles: American Publications.

Maglischo, E. (1982). *Swimming faster: A comprehensive guide to the science of swimming*. Palo Alto, CA: Mayfield.

McGaugh, J.L., & Kiesler, S.B. (Eds.). (1981). *Aging: Biology and behavior*. New York: Academic Press.

Morgan, R.F. (1981). *Measurement of human aging in applied gerontology*. Dubuque, IA: Kendall Hunt.

Parron, D.L., Solomon, F., & Rodin, J. (Eds.). (1981). *Health, behavior and aging*. Institute of Medicine, Washington, DC: National Academic Press.

Pollock, M.L., Miller, H.S., & Wilmore, J. (1974). Physiological characteristics of champion American track athletes 40 to 75 years of age. *Journal of Gerontology*, **29**, 645-649.

Pollock, M.L., Wilmore, J.H., & Fox, S.M. (1984). *Exercise in health and disease*. Philadelphia: Saunders.

Rockstein, M. (Ed.). (1974). *Theoretical aspects of aging*. New York: Academic Press.

Rogers, D. (1982). *The adult years: An introduction to aging* (2nd ed.). Englewood Cliffs, NJ: Prentice-Hall.

Shephard, R.J. (1978). *Physical activity and aging*. Chicago: Yearbook Medical Publishers.

Shephard, R.J. (1981). Cardiovascular limitations in the aged. In E.L. Smith & R.C. Serfass (Eds.), *Exercise and aging: The scientific basis* (pp. 19-29). Hillside, NJ: Enslow.

Shock, N.W. (1974). Physiological theories of aging. In M. Rockstein (Ed.), *Theoretical aspects of aging* (pp. 119-136). New York: Academic Press.

Shock, N.W. (1977). The physiology of aging. In J.R. Barry & C.R. Wingrove (Eds.), *Let's learn about aging* (pp. 61-74). New York: Wiley.

Sidney, K.H., & Shephard, R.J. (1978). Frequency and intensity of exercise training for elderly subjects. *Medicine and Science in Sports and Exercise*, **10**, 125-131.

Sidney, K.H. (1981). Cardiovascular benefits of physical activity in the exercising aged. In E.L. Smith & R.C. Serfass (Eds.), *Exercise and aging: The scientific basis* (pp. 131-147). Hillside, NJ: Enslow.

Silvia, C.E. (1970). *Manual and lesson plans for swimming, life saving, water stunts, springboard diving, and scuba diving and methods of teaching*. Springfield, MA: Author.

Sinclair, A., & Henry, W. (1916). *Swimming*. London: Longmans & Green.

Skinner, J.S. (1970). The cardiovascular system with aging and exercise. In D. Brunner & E. Jokl (Eds.), *Medicine and sport: Physical activity and aging* (pp. 100-108). Basel, Switzerland: S. Karger.

Smith, E.L. (1982). Exercise for prevention of osteoporosis: A review. *The Physician and Sports Medicine*, **10**, 72-83.

Smith, E.L. (1984). *The aging process and the benefits of physical activity*. Unpublished manuscript, The University of Wisconsin.

Smith, E.L., & Gilligan, C. (1983). Physical activity prescription for the older adult. *The Physician and Sports Medicine*, **11**, 91-101.

Smith, E.L., & Serfass, R.C. (Eds.). (1981). *Exercise and aging: The scientific basis*. Hillside, NJ: Enslow.

Thomae, H., & Maddox, G.L. (Eds.). (1982). *New perspectives on old age: A message to decision makers*. New York: Springer.

Timiras, P.S. (1972). *Developmental physiology and aging*. New York: MacMillan.

Uram, P. (1980). *The complete stretching book*. Mountain View, CA: Anderson Word.

Usdin, G., & Hofling, C. (1978). *Aging: The process and the people*. New York: Brunner/Mazel.

Watkin, D.M. (1983). *Handbook of nutrition, health and aging*. Park Ridge, NJ: Noyes.

Whitehouse, F.A. (1977). Motivation for fitness. In R. Harris & L.J. Frankel (Eds.), *Guide to fitness after fifty* (pp. 171-189). New York: Plenum Press.

Wilmore, J.H. (1982). *Training for sport and activity: The physiological basis of the conditioning process* (2nd ed.). Boston: Allyn & Bacon.

Wiswell, R.A. (1980). Relaxation, exercise and aging. In J.E. Birren & E. Sloane (Eds.), *Handbook of mental health and aging* (pp. 938-949). Englewood Cliffs, NJ: Prentice-Hall.

INDEX